A Song
for Molly

# A Song for Molly

### Jeremy Bernstein

Stevens Institute of Technology, USA

**World Scientific**

NEW JERSEY · LONDON · SINGAPORE · BEIJING · SHANGHAI · HONG KONG · TAIPEI · CHENNAI · TOKYO

*Published by*

World Scientific Publishing Co. Pte. Ltd.

5 Toh Tuck Link, Singapore 596224

*USA office:* 27 Warren Street, Suite 401-402, Hackensack, NJ 07601

*UK office:* 57 Shelton Street, Covent Garden, London WC2H 9HE

Library of Congress Control Number: 2020945737

**British Library Cataloguing-in-Publication Data**
A catalogue record for this book is available from the British Library.

ISBN 978-981-121-819-4 (hardcover)
ISBN 978-981-121-894-1 (paperback)
ISBN 978-981-121-820-0 (ebook for institutions)
ISBN 978-981-121-821-7 (ebook for individuals)

For any available supplementary material, please visit
https://www.worldscientific.com/worldscibooks/10.1142/11769#t=suppl

Typeset by Stallion Press
Email: enquiries@stallionpress.com

# Preface

What are little boys made of?
Slugs and snails
And puppy-dogs' tails,
Slugs and snails
And puppy-dogs' tails,
That's what little boys are made of.
What are little girls made of?
What are little girls made of?
Sugar and spice
And everything nice,
That's what little girls are made of.

Myths are things that never were but always are,
*Il en savait ce qu'on a su dans tous les ages; c'est-a'- dire, fort peu des choses*

Voltaire

Over the years I have written short fiction stories — from time to time. The most successful ones were published in places like *The New Yorker, The American Scholar, The Gettysburg Review,* and *The Mountain Gazette.* This was a congenial form for me since when I began one, I had no idea how it would end. The endings came as much of a surprise to me as to the reader. This novel or novella also began as a short story. But it began with certain observations. I live in Greenwich Village and I frequently go to a coffee shop near both NYU and Washington Square Park. It has long windows which enable you to look out at the sidewalk. Every time I went there, I could observe women with their dogs, often the same woman with the same dog. One woman had three small brown dogs on leashes. They look very nice, but like most of the dogs I observe, they seem to have a different agenda from that of their mistress. She wants to get them to the park as quickly as possible, give them time to tend to their affairs, and then get them back home. The dogs, on the contrary, want to stop and explore. They also want to mark the postbox in front of the coffee shop as part of their territory. She tries to tug them along on their leashes while they go off in various directions. She of course wins, but not without a struggle.

One morning as I was watching this, a fantasy occurred to me. I imagined that an attractive woman came with a dog and sat on the bench outside the coffee shop. I stopped paying attention but the dog walked in dragging its leash. I took the dog and its leash outside to return it to the woman but she was gone. It became clear that the dog had been abandoned and that her name was Molly. In my fantasy I took her home and you can read what happened. Somehow in all of this Wittgenstein makes his appearance. I have always thought that he was taken much too seriously so in my story, he is not. I should tell you that my acquaintance with him, or at least his work, goes back a long way. When I was a Harvard junior, I took a reading course with the physicist philosopher Philipp Frank. We read together Wittgenstein's *Tractatus*. The copy I have says inside the cover "J. Bernstein, At Harvard, Spring 1950." I learned that Professor Frank had been a member of the Vienna Circle — a mixed group of intellectuals who met sometimes in coffee shops in Vienna to discuss various topics in philosophy and science. They studied the *Tractatus* when Wittgenstein was a member, but he was of no use since he sat to one side reading poetry. Kurt Gödel was also a member for a while. He gave it up because he disagreed with their views on the nature of mathematics. Gödel is an important figure in my story. One of the things I describe actually happened. In the fall of my first year, at the Institute for Advanced Study, Oppenheimer decided that we should have a dance. No one danced but out of the corner of my eye I could see Oppenheimer with Gödel in tow. How he had persuaded him to come I cannot imagine. When I was introduced to him, he said to me "I knew your father in Vienna." I told him that my father had never been to Vienna and Gödel repeated, "I knew your father in Vienna." I gave up.

I have no intention of deconstructing my story to pick out the real parts but I would like to say something about Doctor Levman, the psychiatrist. I did see a psychiatrist for a while and I did ask him if he was a Freudian and he did say that he thought Freud was a very quotable fellow. I once gave him a story of mine that eventually found its way into *The New Yorker*. When he gave it back to me he said that it was better than he thought it was going to be, which I took as a compliment. I miss him.

On a final note, I would like to thank Ken Ford for his careful reading on subsequent drafts of the book; his help and encouragement was valuable to its completion.

# Contents

# Chapter *1*

*Die Welt is alles, was der fall ist* — The world is everything that is the case.

Ludwig Wittgenstein

"Why can't a dog simulate pain? Is he too honest? Could one teach a dog to simulate pain? Perhaps it is possible to teach him to howl on particular occasions as if he were in pain, even when he is not. But the surroundings which are necessary for this behavior to be real simulation are missing."

Ludwig Wittgenstein

I

In the mornings, I go to a nearby coffee shop frequented by students. It is run by some Asians who speak no language recognizable to me. Since most of its customers are students, the prices are reasonable. There is also a large picture window. Perched on a stool, I can observe the passersby. The other day, an elegant woman stopped near my window. She was very well dressed. At her foot was a small brown dog. I could not help but try to picture the relationship of this women with her dog. How do they communicate?

The first time I went to India, an Indian friend of mine said that each day you will see something that you will not understand. He was right and

I feel the same way about women. When you are around them, each day they do something I do not understand. I find that it is no use asking for an explanation. As far as they are concerned, it is like trying to explain the color orange to someone who is colorblind. There is a bench in front of the window through which I have been gazing. The woman has sat down on it and is now dissolved in tears. That is a curious verb here — dissolved. If tears could melt, this poor woman would have melted. Seeing women cry breaks my heart. I heard my mother cry only once. My father had told her that we were moving cities because of his job. We would be leaving the house, that into which she had poured her love — the garden, and the living room with its special sofa. It was too big to move. I was 10 and outside the door. I have never forgotten. I would like to comfort this woman as I would have liked to have comforted my mother. But there are rules.

While I am reflecting on this, the door to the coffee shop is opened by a student who is followed by the dog who is trailing its leash. There is a sign on the door insisting that people do not bring pets into the coffee shop. One might argue that the dog was not brought in but came in of its own accord. In any event, insofar as this was a problem, the solution seemed simple. I will take the dog by its leash and return it to its owner. Then I could finish my pecan roll on the bench and perhaps even offer some comfort to the woman. The problem was that she had disappeared. Probably, I thought, she was looking for the dog.

I sat down on the bench and the dog lay down at my feet. After twenty minutes, there was no sign of the woman so I looked at the tag on the dog's collar. The dog's name is Molly, and there is a phone number to call if you find the dog. When I called the number, I found that it had been disconnected. Molly, it seems clear to me, has been abandoned. I have to tell you that I never had a dog. When we lived in the big house with the garden, my mother said that my baby sister was too small to have a dog around, and when we shifted to our new house, an apartment, it was too small. But it seems to me that I am about to have a dog. I can't just leave her here. I will take her home. But I have no idea what to feed her to say the least. There is a pet shop on my way home. It is called "Paws" a name I find nauseating. Why not "Claws"? But there is nothing for it but to go there and get something for Molly to eat. I have no idea what kind of dog Molly is to say nothing of her age. I think she is too sedentary to be a puppy. The man in the store suggests dry "bits." The ingredient list is mind-boggling. There are things like chicken meal and brewer's rice. I have no idea what those are. There are additives like alpha-tocopherol acetate and inositol. It sounds to me that given to humans, a doctor's prescription would be required. Given the general human condition with most of the world starving, what sense does this make? Anyway, I buy a large bag for Molly and a bowl in which to put water and a rubber bone if she needs a toy. I also buy a few "treats" in case Molly would like a snack. When I enter my apartment building, the doorman asks if I have bought a dog. I explain that I am only taking care of it for a few days for a friend. Molly does not seem to have much curiosity about my apartment. She finds a comfortable spot on the rug and falls asleep.

I have no idea at what time Molly is accustomed to eat. The man in the store said that twice a day is about right. I would imagine that Molly has had breakfast so I will wait until tonight. She does drink quite a lot of water so I decide to take her to the park for a walk. There is a dog place which I always avoid, but maybe Molly would feel at home there. When we get there, I am a bit surprised when she shows no interest in playing with other dogs. She just lies down and goes to sleep. When it is time to go home, I call her name and she gets up and walks in front of me. When it is what I think is her dinner time I put some bits in her bowl. She takes a few perfunctory bites and again goes to sleep. I guess she has had a hard day.

Molly has now been with me for over a week. Our routine is pretty much the same day after day. We go for our walks. She will still not play with other dogs and tends to go to sleep. She doesn't seem to eat a lot. I have tried different things including a few bones. She looks like she is getting a little thinner. Sometimes she comes over to where I am working and looks up at me as if she is trying to tell me something. I wish that I knew. Maybe she is not feeling well. I will take her to a vet. Some friends of mine know one and say that he is very nice. I make an appointment. Doctor Snyder puts her on a table where he can look her over. Then he takes some blood. Molly does not protest. I wonder if she has done this before. Doctor Snyder says he will call me in a few days.

I have hardly ever cried. Even when my mother died I did not cry. I could not cry. After Doctor Snyder called, I cried. I dissolved in tears. Molly is not going to live very long. I will keep her with me as long as she is well enough and then let her go. I now understand why the woman I saw that day was crying. She knew.

II

I know a lot of jokes. I seem to have a flypaper memory for jokes. I even remember some from when I was a kid. What has four wheels and flies? A garbage truck. You would also call a neighbor and say you were from the electric company. "Is your streetlight on?" "Yes." Well don't forget to turn it off before you go to bed." That kind of thing. Now I do an exercise. I think of a topic at random and see if I can find a joke that goes with it. Fish. A man steals a fish from a fish monger and hides it in his coat but the tail is sticking out. The fish monger says "Next time steal a shorter fish or buy a longer coat." Sometimes I make up jokes. What does an Indian say to a mermaid? "How?" Some things are beyond jokes. The death of Molly for example. She got so sick that I had to take her to the vet to be put down. That is the phrase they use, "put down." Do they put people down?

I know a great scholar of the East and Near East. I raised the following with him. Laughter I am sure is universal but are jokes? He told me that the farthest east he was able to trace jokes to was Persia. There are no Indian jokes, no Chinese jokes, and no Japanese jokes. I never heard of a Japanese stand-up. "A funny thing happened to me on the way to the Sento." Of course things have changed, you can buy a book on Indian limericks. But they are all similar, just with a change of name and place — "There was a young man from Bengal" — that kind of thing. Europeans all have jokes. They usually bring into the light some darkened area of the psyche. Maybe

Oriental people believe that it is better to let sleeping dogs lie. Speaking of the psyche, I went to see a psychiatrist for a while. I had just broken up with a woman who said that I should have my head examined. Some friends gave me the name of the psychiatrist. My first visit was quite odd. His office was in his house, but there were separate flights of stairs for going up and stairs for going down so patients would never meet. He asked me why I was there. I said that I was not really sure. He said who do you talk to when you have problems. I said that sometimes I talk to friends. He said that talking to him would probably not be less useful than talking to them, I asked if he was a Freudian. He said that Freud was a "very quotable fellow." I felt that we would get along. We always sat facing each other. He generally kept his eyes closed and looked like a very observant and deceptively sleepy cat — cat whiskers and all. When I came for a visit, he always asked what I had been thinking and feeling. At first I could not think of anything to say but by the end I was in tears. I was grateful for the flight of stairs that headed to the ground floor. He died, otherwise I would talk to him about Molly.

Doctor Levman, that was his name, and I discussed marriage. Put more accurately, Doctor Levman wanted to know why I was not married. I told him that when I thought of marriage all I could think of was a large cage in which I was trapped but got fed three times a day. "That doesn't leave much room for sex," Doctor Levman said. "If you want a Jewish girl to stop having sex, just marry her," I answered. "What is your idea of the ideal woman?" he asked. "We have great sex until midnight and then she turns into a pizza," I answered. "Do you really mean that?" he asked. "Not really," I answered, "I don't much like pizzas."

The woman who had dumped me had what had become a familiar complaint — lack of commitment — the cage again. She once said to me, "You are the only man I ever loved and you won't marry me." At the time she said it, she was legally separated from her first husband. Didn't she love him? She wanted a child, she said. There were times when we walked by stores for baby things, and she would insist that we stop and look into the window. She said that I should give up my apartment and move in with her. I was never going to give up my apartment. It was my escape hatch. I explained this to Doctor Levman, who asked why I needed an escape hatch. "To keep from drowning," I said. I guess she was right to dump me. She got married twice again and never had a child so I don't know what to think. I wonder if Molly ever had any puppies.

I told Doctor Levman a psychiatrist joke. He pretended that he had not heard it before. A man goes to see a psychiatrist and says "Doctor I feel inferior." The psychiatrist says, "Your problem is that you are inferior." I don't feel inferior but I don't feel superior either. I am average height and a little overweight. My hair is turning gray. I do have a very good memory. I remember things that people — especially women — have said to me for years and years afterwards. I can play them in my head like a CD.

Here is a thought. Imagine that Isaac Newton comes back to life and starts to wander around New York. Of course, you would have to take him to Brooks Brothers first and get him a decent suit so he wouldn't look like a freak. What would surprise him most? Of course, there is the obvious — the cars, the lights, all those sorts of things. But what I think he would have the most difficulty to understand are people talking loudly into small black rectangles. Of course, in his day there would be the odd nut talking into thin air. But this? What it has done is to erode our sense of privacy. People talk publicly on their cell phones about almost anything. It seems to have slopped over into general discourse.

The other morning I was in the coffee shop. Two women were sitting right next to me. They were nicely dressed and looked like they were professional people. They were talking fairly loudly to each other about menopause. They described their periods and their hot-flashes. They must have known that I was listening. I could not help but listen. I was tempted to join the conversation. Almost all women that I have known do not like their bodies. In fact, I wonder if there is any woman who likes her body. I like their bodies but that does not count. I once said to a woman, "it seems very hard to be a woman." "Not if you are good at it," she answered, "and I am." It is a lot easier to be a dog.

## III

My friend Anne once said to me, "I do not know what a barge pole is but I wouldn't touch you with one. You are the typhoid Mary of relationships. Only you would find a female dog who would die on you in two weeks and break your heart," I explained that I did not find Molly. In a manner of speaking she found me. "That's what you said about that model who used to call you at two in the morning and ask if Germany was the country that had an East and West Germany." "She had an interest in geography," I answered.

"What ever happened to her?" Anne asked. "The last time I heard from her it was a letter from a mental hospital which began 'I no longer hear voices.'" "What did you see in her?" Anne asked. "She had a body like a Greek statue," I replied. "You men, it is amazing you can get anything done. You keep stumbling over your libidos." To change the subject I told her something I had heard about General de Gaulle. He was given a turtle and he asked how long it would live. He was told about one hundred and fifty years. "Just when you learn to love them," he said, "They die." I wonder how old Molly was when she died. Then I told Anne about Pilates.

I used to go to the studio on 6th Avenue when Pilates himself ran it. They had a strict dress code. You had to wear ballet slippers and plain T-shirts. One day I came in with one which read, "Good girls go to heaven. Bad girls go everywhere." I was told to change it. Pilates was short and constructed like a fire plug. He had a German accent and one glass eye. He would fix it on you when he said, "Vee train your mind." The changing room was somewhat primitive. Men and women were separated by a barrier of lockers which were not very tightly joined. You could catch a glimpse of the women in various stages of undress. I suppose they could have caught glimpse of us likewise. I could imagine looking through one of the separations and seeing the eye of someone looking through the other side. It never happened. But you could listen to the conversations.

They were a never-ending source of amazement. They might go something like this.

Woman 1: That is a lovely ring.

Woman 2: My fiancé gave it to me.

Woman 1: How long have you been engaged?

Woman 2: About three years. He is becoming a dentist.

Woman1: Are you living together?

Woman 2: No. He is living with his mother.

You could write a whole novel about this doomed couple. The men on the other side of the partition merely grunted at each other in passing. I asked Anne about this. "Women know what matters," she explained.

## IV

Have you noticed this change in discourse? If you say in a store, for example, "Thank you" to a clerk, the response isn't "Don't mention it," but rather "It's not a problem." Why should it be a problem? I imagine leaving an orgy and the hostess saying, "Thank you for coming," to which I respond, "It's not a problem, May I come again." The 1960s, at least in New York, were a kind of orgy. I refer to this period as the PPPA era — Post Pill Pre-Aids. Most of what you could pick up you could cure. I am not sure that I was ever told the name of some of the women I slept with. I have a vivid memory of November 9, 1965. I had been invited to a party and had gone into the bathroom to use my electric razor. The light over the basin did not go on. I went to change the bulb when I realized that there were no lights. The whole city was dark. The phone worked so I called my friend to ask if the party was still on. "Absolutely," he said. I walked several blocks to his place and found it full and candlelit. I got talking to a girl and when it came time to leave she came with me. I am not even sure I had asked. No one wanted to be alone. There was a full moon and it was a warm fall night. We held hands for reassurance. When we got to my place we had to walk up eighteen flights of stairs. People were coming up and down the stairs with flashlights. I said to her that some of them looked like Diogenes who wandered around ancient Greece with a lantern looking for an honest man.

We spent the night and the next morning I walked her down the stairs and never saw her again.

Diogenes was a "Cynic" — *kynikos* — dog-like. Dogs are "shameless" and go about in a state of nature. So did Diogenes. Dogs can distinguish between friends and enemies instinctively. I am quite sure that Molly thought of me as a friend. Maybe I should have let her die in my arms, but she was so sick. And Wittgenstein — what was he on about? Teach a dog to howl even when it is not in pain — why? Wittgenstein — there was an odd dude.

Wittgenstein and Hitler were born six days apart in 1889. Both attended the *Realschule* — a technical high school — at the same time. Hitler had been held back a year while Wittgenstein had been moved up by one. If they ever met, they would have disliked each other intensely. Hitler spoke German with a Bavarian accent, while Wittgenstein spoke an especially pure form of High German with a stutter. What a pair they would have made. Wittgenstein while baptized as a Catholic became Jewish after the racial laws of his schoolmate. If Wittgenstein had only taken Hitler home for a visit to one of the Wittgenstein mansions — they were one of the richest families in Europe — history might have been changed. "Adolph I would like you to meet my father Karl and my sister Margaret…" Suppose Hitler had married Margaret — the one who was painted by Klimmt — how many lives might have been spared. As it is, Hitler was kicked out of the school for bad behavior. Wittgenstein was an excellent student except for spelling. He simply could not learn how to spell.

Hitler played the piano and Wittgenstein took up the clarinet in his thirties. If Hitler had only been invited to the Wittgensteins, he could have met people like Mahler, Brahms, and Bruno Walter, who frequently gave concerts there. He might have gotten to know Wittgenstein's brother Paul, who was a concert pianist. When he lost his right arm in the First World War, he commissioned Ravel to write his Concerto for the Left Hand. Speak of making do with adversity. Wittgenstein and Hitler were on the same side in that war, although Wittgenstein was a much decorated officer and a prisoner of war. Three of his brothers committed suicide. I have not been able to learn if the family kept dogs.

Anne has shown up in the coffee shop wearing an eggshell blue, long-sleeved T-shirt with a photograph of Wittgenstein in front. He is staring out with those coal black raven eyes.

I asked her why she was wearing it. "I know you have a thing about Wittgenstein and besides he was quite good looking." "His sexuality was a bit mixed up," I said. "He was both AC and DC. He went off to Iceland with a Cambridge undergraduate in mathematics and bought him clothes. He also hired a private train. In 1913 his father died and Wittgenstein became one of the richest men in Europe. He gave a lot of the money away. He later proposed to a Swiss woman on the condition they never have children. She left town."

The year 1918 was quite a year for Wittgenstein. He had completed his *Tractatus Logico Philosophicus* — the book that made his reputation. He had worked on it while he was a prisoner of war in Italy. His brother Kurt committed suicide. The young man he had gone to Iceland with was killed in a plane crash. He dedicated the *Tractatus* to him. Wittgenstein decided to give all his money away to his remaining siblings and become an elementary school teacher. He had been to Cambridge before the war and had gotten to know Bertrand Russell, so when the *Tractatus* was finally translated into English in 1923, Russell wrote an introduction to it. The book is a series of propositions which are numbered. The English translation and the original German appear on opposite pages. For example, proposition 5.600 reads

> *Die Grenzen meiner Sprache bedeuten die Grenzen meiner Welt — The limits of my language means the limits of my world.*

This is not exactly something you can build a code of conduct out of. It sounds more like a teenage statement of possession.

Anne asks me if she should try to read it. "You would have to have a high tolerance for statements like 'not(not vanilla and not chocolate)' means the same thing as 'vanilla or chocolate.'" "Why?" she asks. I am not sure what she is referring to but whatever it is I do not have a good answer for her.

**V**

Wittgenstein tried to use an assumed name when he applied for his teaching jobs. If they had known that he was a "Wittgenstein," that would have raised a lot of suspicions. Maybe he was crazy or some kind of pervert. He must have had a good deal of time on his hands because he read *The Brothers Karamazov* over several times. I wonder if he could keep the names straight. The hero — Alexei Fyodorovich Karamazov — appears in the book as Alyosha, Alyoshka, Alyoshenka, Alyoshecka, Alexeichik, Lyosha, and Lyoshenka. It sounds like the declension of an irregular verb, *fero, ferre, tuli,* and *latus.* Maybe he identified with one of the characters — possibly Alyosha who was also having problems with his brothers. Wittgenstein was certainly not into murdering his father for the money since he gave it away as soon as he could.

Wittgenstein raised the question of whether a dog can be trained to be insincere. Can, for example, it learn to cry out in pain even when it isn't feeling any? One would have to get across to the dog the reasons for doing this; a treat or a pat on the head. I think of this when I pass the pet store where I used to buy food for Molly. There is a big picture window in front, and behind it, there are always two or three puppies cavorting on what looks like confetti. I suppose they spend the night in a kennel in the shop. They must have an odd view of the cosmos. Why, they might wonder, are we spending this time at the back of this window? They have no idea that if someone buys them, their lives will take a quantum leap. If they are lucky, a nice family will buy them and take them to the beach. If one could communicate with them about this, they might learn to do things to make themselves more attractive to buyers. One of them might come to the window and extend a paw. As it is, they simply romp around. I think Molly was sincere. What you saw was what you got. At the end she could not give much, though she tried.

## VI

Despite my attempts to caution her, Anne is trying to read the *Tractatus*. She is annoyed with me because she is having a difficult time understanding it as if this was my fault. I asked if she had read Wittgenstein's preface where he says that it may be that only people who have already had similar thoughts can understand it. "What a stupid idea," she says. "If I had had similar thoughts what would I need him for." "Isn't that what friends are for?" I asked. "With a friend like Wittgenstein…." she answers. To cheer her up, I said that some things in the *Tractatus* seem to me to be simply wrong. For example, take note of what he says about hieroglyphics.

*4.016 Um das Wesen der Satzes zu vershtehn, denken wir an die Hieroglyphenschrift, welche die Tataschen die sie beschrift abbildet.*
*"In order to understand the essence of the proposition, consider hieroglyphic writing which pictures the facts that it describes.*

The problem is that this is not what hieroglyphic writing mostly does. Take the example of ducks. The symbol that looks like a duck but has a vertical line stands for a duck, but if it doesn't have a vertical line, then it stands for a syllable.

duck                    *sa*

The Egyptians had a syllabic alphabet. They never bothered to get it down to letters. If one thinks about it, there had to be something like this. How otherwise would you be able to refer to an individual without drawing his or her picture.

"Why did Wittgenstein get into this especially if he did not know what he was talking about?" Anne asked.

"He had a pictorial view of propositions," I replied. "Take his 4.06 'Propositions can be true or false only by being pictures of reality'."

"But what about his propositions about language? They were in the language he was trying to picture."

I had to admit that this was a logical cleft stick. Bertrand Russell suggested that these propositions had to be couched in a meta-language but then propositions about this language had to be expressed in a higher meta-language so you were stuck in an infinite regress. I explained that Wittgenstein understood this and at the end of the Tractatus he expresses his doubt about the whole enterprise. He says that anyone who understands him realizes that his propositions are senseless. That last one 6.34 reads

*Wovon man nicht sprechen kann darüber muss man schweigen.*
*"Whereof one cannot speak, thereof one must be silent."*

"That is just like a man," Anne notes. "He writes a whole book about something that he says he cannot write about. No woman would do such a stupid thing."

## VII

I had a dream last night. In it Molly has gone to see Doctor Levman. She must have made an appointment because Doctor Levman is very strict about that sort of thing. She climbs up those stairs and Doctor Levman tells her to sit down in the chair that I used to sit down in. He wants to know something about her. Molly tells him that her first memories are of being in a pet shop and looking out the picture window. She had no idea of how she got there or what she was supposed to do. But a couple came in and took her to their apartment. They had prepared for her arrival with a water bowl and some kind of bed she could sleep on, although she preferred to sleep on the rug. The food was very good and one of them took her out a couple of times a day so she could go to the park. There were other dogs there she could play with. She was quite happy. But then the couple started to fight. It was so bad that she used to hide under the bed. The man left and the woman cried a lot. Molly said that she used to try to do tricks to make the woman stop crying but then she got sick and the woman cried even more. Molly could no longer do her tricks. Then one day the woman took her out and just left her.

"How did you feel?" Doctor Levman asked.

"Awful," Molly replied, "but another man took me to his place."

"What was he like?" Doctor Levman asked.

"He was very nice but I was too sick to do many tricks. I wondered why he lived alone."

"That's what I wondered," Doctor Levman said.

"Did you figure it out?" Molly asked.

"Not really but I tried to make him think about it."

Then I woke up.

## VIII

Wittgenstein once asked a friend, "Why did people believe that the Sun went around the Earth?" The friend answered, "Because it looked that way?" Wittgenstein then asked, "How would it have looked if it had been the other way around?" Wittgenstein was much concerned with a curious aspect of language. You could form sentences in which every word had a meaning but the sentence was meaningless. Not only was the whole less than the sum of the parts, but the whole was zero. He gave as an example, "Socrates was identical." He felt that much of academic philosophy consisted of arguments about propositions like this. As it happened, there was a group of scientist-philosophers in Vienna at the time who agreed with him. They had begun before the war as a few friends who met in Viennese coffee houses to discuss how to rid modern science of metaphysics. The discussions were aided by some *Linzer Torte* and *Kaffe mit Schlag*. But during the war the group was disbanded to be reconstituted under somewhat more formal circumstances at the University of Vienna. The called themselves the *Wiener Kreis* — the Vienna Circle. They decided to write a small scientific encyclopedia. After the *Tractatus* was published, they decided that they had to understand it so they went over it line by line. At this time, Wittgenstein was living in Vienna but working as a gardener. He was also helping to design his sister's house. Once when a ceiling did not look quite right, he had it torn down. He was invited to join the Circle. He came to some meetings where he sat reading poetry. From time to time, he would make a seer-like utterance. He decided that he and they were on different pages and quit coming to meetings. Science was never Wittgenstein's strong suit. The references to it in the *Tractatus* have to do with Newton and Darwin. He apparently had no interest in Einstein.

In 1929, Wittgenstein returned to Cambridge. Keynes met him and wrote to his wife, "Well God has arrived. I met him on 5:15 train." There was a problem. He had no academic degree. He was told to submit the *Tractatus* as a PhD thesis. His examiners were Bertrand Russell and the moral philosopher G.E. Moore. As he turned in the *Tractatus*, he said that neither of them would be able to understand it. In his report, Moore wrote "I myself consider that this is a work of genius, but even if I am completely mistaken, and it is nothing of the sort, it is well above the standard required for the PhD degree." In 1939, after Moore retired, Wittgenstein succeeded him as a Professor of Philosophy. He gave what he called lectures, but they were more like disjointed utterances. One of the students noted that "His face was lean and brown, his profile was aquiline and strikingly beautiful, his head was covered with a curly mass of brown hair, but I observed the respectful attention that everyone in the room paid to him."

Wittgenstein took up residence at Trinity College. As it happens, I know someone who after the war also became a resident of Trinity. He lived on the same stairwell. There was food rationing at the time so my friend cooked his own dinners and he could smell the fish that Wittgenstein was cooking. Day after day they passed each other on the stairwell and said nothing. But one day Wittgenstein suddenly invited my friend for coffee to his room. There was one chair — a sort of deck chair — in which my friend sat. Wittgenstein said nothing. My friend who had read the *Tractatus* when he was a teenager decided that he should say something. He asked Wittgenstein if he had changed his mind about anything he had written in the *Tractatus* to which Wittgenstein replied, "Tell me which newspaper do you represent?" ending the conversation.

## IX

The *Tractatus* has brought Anne and me closer. We struggle over propositions like,

> *Was sich in der Sprache ausdrückt, konnen wir nicht durch sie ausdrücken. —* "That which expresses itself in language, we cannot express by language,"

I wonder if the proposition

"That which does not express *itself* in language, we can express by language" could be equally valid. We need guidance.

Sometimes Anne tells me that I should get another dog. Maybe I will, but it is too soon. I am still grieving for Molly. But last night I had a dream about Wittgenstein. He had gone to see Doctor Levman. Doctor Levman asked, "Why are you here?" and Wittgenstein replied "What do you mean by 'why?'" Doctor Levman says, "You do not seem very friendly. Remember what you wrote in your Philosophical Grammar. 'A friendly mouth, friendly eyes, the wagging of a dog's tail are primary symbols of friendliness; they are parts of the phenomenon that are called friendliness'. 'You do not seem to have 'friendly eyes'." Wittgenstein is surprised by this. He is not used to dialogue with students. He is also annoyed by a reference to dogs. "You need a dog," Doctor Levman says. Before Wittgenstein can respond, I wake up. I have decided to go with Anne to the pet store and look at dogs.

# Chapter 2

"In the discussions of the provability of mathematical propositions it is sometimes said that there are substantial propositions of mathematics whose truth or falsehood must remain undecided. What the people who say that don't realize is that such propositions, *if* we can use them and want to call them 'propositions', are not at all the same as what are called 'propositions' in other cases; because a proof alters the grammar of a proposition. You can certainly use one and the same piece of wood first as a weathervane and *then* as a signpost; but you can't use it fixed as a weathervane and moving as a signpost. If someone wanted to say 'There are also moving signposts' I would answer 'You really mean "There are moving *pieces of wood*." I don't say that a moving piece of wood can't possibly be used at all but only that it can't be used as a signpost."

*Philosophical Grammar* by Ludwig Wittgenstein, p. 367

"Are we to think that 2+2 is not 4 but 4.01?"

Bertrand Russell in a letter to Leon Henkin

"Has Wittgenstein lost his mind? Does he mean it seriously? He intentionally utters trivially nonsensical statements ..."

Kurt Gödel, in *A Logical Journey* by Hao Wang, p. 179

# I

I have gone with Anne to Paws to pick out a dog. I have no idea what kind of dog Molly was, but I want a female puppy that looks something like what I imagine Molly must have looked like when she was young. There are a bunch of puppies playing in the window. One of them stops and looks at me. I wish I knew what she was thinking, but I decide that this is the dog I will buy. Anne approves. We get a lot of supplies including a carrier so we can take the puppy back to my apartment without her running away or getting scared. This seems acceptable to the puppy. When she gets to the apartment, she explores. She then decides to take a nap on my bed which is all right with me. Anne wishes us luck.

The first problem I have to deal with is how to teach her what her name is. You have the same problem with human babies, but they have a period of echolalia. They will echo things you say which can be unnerving. "Would you like to go to bed?" "Would you like to go to bed?" "Would you like to go to bed?" "Now?" I have been reading about dogs and have decided to try an experiment. I say to the puppy, "Your name is Molly," and then give the puppy a treat. The puppy seems delighted. I then say "Your name is not Molly," and give her a treat which she happily accepts. This is not progress. I decide to take Molly out for a walk.

I manage to put a collar on her with a name tag so she can be returned to me if she wanders off. I try to explain this to her but her behavior is so far consistent with the Chomskyan notion of "language acquisition device" (LAD). She doesn't have one. No animal has. All humans have them, even the San Bush people who communicate with a click language. What seem to be words are punctuated with intermittent clicks. The babies also acquire these clicks. Maybe all our first languages were click languages. I watched an interview of these people by someone from the National Geographic. He said how honored he was to have been accorded this interview. He was very nicely dressed in what he probably thought of as a bush outfit. The few, somewhat scraggly bush people who were there — not many are left — clicked something. He asked for the word for "one." A click word was provided. He asked for the word for "two" and another word was provided — then "three". He quit there, which was a pity. Some of these African languages only go up to "two." It is "one, two, many". If he had gone up to "four" he might have learned something. Deaf children were left on their own to teach themselves some sort of sign language that can be quite sophisticated. They will never teach themselves to read.

There is a theory of why animals do not talk which I like. It is evolutionary. Let us apply it to wolves and dogs. In the early days, there were no dogs — only wolves and they could speak. Our ancestors went into the forest and found these wolves with whom they could carry on a conversation. The wolves wanted to know who these odd bipeds were and why they were carrying sharp sticks. They asked, and instead of being given a sensible answer, they were put in cages and taken away. Some were killed for their pelts and others were simply eaten. None of them could breed. Now back in the forest there was the odd wolf who because of a mutation was unable to speak. He had acquired a language suppressor gene. These wolves were left alone and could breed. After a few generations, there were no talking wolves. But some of the non-talking wolves were taken into captivity and treated better. They did breed and evolved into our dogs. I like this theory, but it raises a question. Millions and millions of dogs have been bred, but none of them, as far as I know, has a mutation that restores speech. Why not? Maybe some of them could talk, but their owners decided not to tell anyone so they wouldn't have to bother with the reporters. It is also possible that the dogs did not tell their owners they could talk because they liked the status quo. Maybe Molly is holding out on me and at some point we can have a conversation. In the meanwhile, we will have to make do.

I explain to Molly about the leash. I tell her that we are going into the park to play and that I am worried about losing her. We practice walking around the apartment with the leash. I tell her a joke with the punch line no dog should go out on a night like this. I give her some treats and she seems ok with it. She is a little hesitant about leaving the apartment.

Apart from the pet shop, it is the only home she has known. I walk ahead down the hall, and she follows me. She also follows me into the elevator and out the front door of the apartment house. Once on the street, Molly looks somewhat bewildered. There is so much going on that I can hardly blame her. I give her a reassuring hug. We first walk past Paws. Molly shows no interest, and the puppies in the window seem not to notice. Then we walk past the coffee shop where all this started. Molly shows no interest. She is concentrated on the legs of a green post box on the corner. I have a theory about this post box. It has its collection hours — 4 pm on weekdays and 1:30 pm on Saturdays — posted on the outside. My theory is that mail is never collected from this box. It is a practical joke by the post office. If you could get inside you would find things like Christmas cards and wedding invitations put in there at least a decade earlier. People would have phoned Con Edison insisting that they had mailed in their checks. Molly decides to micturate on one of the legs. She is marking her territory, but I find the post box an odd choice. Maybe it is Molly's idea of a practical joke.

In the park, there is a fenced-off area for dogs. You make sure that the gates are closed after you walk in because the dogs run around freely and one does not want them to run away. I take Molly's leash off. She looks at me as if to say, "Make up your mind." She has never been around such a collection of dogs. She had a social life at Paws, but all the other dogs were puppies like her. Some of the dogs in the park are enormous. They make me nervous. She takes a few steps and then comes back for a pat. She may be worried that I might go away and leave her. Then she gets bolder and soon she is romping around with the other dogs. She makes a friend and brings him over to me. I give both of them a treat. Her friend seems to be about the same age. An elegant woman comes over following her dog — Molly's new friend. She sits down, and we watch the two dogs. There is a French phrase that I like, *donner un ticket*. If a woman makes a pass at you say, *Elle m'a donne' un ticket* — it is a ticket to ride the train. It is like a magic trick. You know it has been done, but you don't quite know how and you never let on that you know you have been given a ticket. That would spoil everything.

The woman's name is Elena, and her dog's name is Stanley. She is a widow of a few years, and her husband's name was Stanley. Stanley the dog is an avatar of Stanley the man, and Molly the dog is an avatar of Molly the dog. I pretend that I do not notice that Elena has given me a ticket. She can hardly say, "I have given you a ticket, why don't you climb aboard?" I will let her make up her own theories. The reason for my hesitation is that I can predict the future. I have been here before. She will invite me to her apartment for dinner. Everything will be perfect — candles and all and we will go to bed. Molly has come with me and she and Stanley can remain in the kitchen. We will have a relationship. Our dogs will have a relationship. But I know that there is a "mean life" — the average amount of time before commitment comes into the situation like a shroud. It is usually about two months, but it can be longer or shorter. I am told that our relationship is stuck. It is not advancing. I see it as a large vehicle with its tires spinning in the mud. The word "commitment" is suspended over the exposed neck of our relationship like the sword of Damocles. Nothing will pull this vehicle out of the ooze. Tears are inevitable, and all I want to do is to go home and put my head on or under a pillow. In this case, Molly and Stanley will never see each other again. I am determined not to go down this path now. I will bring Anne to the dog park, and she and Elena can have a good soul-searching talk. Perhaps she can convince Elena that she has had a narrow escape.

## II

I have had a dream. Molly has gone to see Doctor Levman. She has climbed the stairs in his brownstone house — the ones reserved for patients. She has seated herself in the same chair I used to sit in when I saw Doctor Levman. She has a question for Doctor Levman. It has to do with me. She wants to know if Doctor Levman can explain why I live alone. "Don't most people have mates," she asks. "Yes", says Doctor Levman, "I do not understand why he does not have a mate, but now he has you." "But", Molly answers, "I am only a dog."

## III

Two men who have not seen each other for a while meet.

"How are things going Sam?"
"Terribly."
"Oh?"
"My business is going bankrupt."
"It could be worse."
"My son is on drugs."
"It could be worse."
"My wife is leaving me."
"It could be worse."
"How could it possibly be worse?"
"It could be happening to me."

A woman in the coffee shop I have just left is talking to an older man with a beard. He reminds me of Doctor Levman. She is pouring her heart out, and he is listening carefully and not saying much. Finally, she says, "He will just have to adapt to reality." I am ashamed to admit that all I can think of is "It could be happening to me."

## IV

Anne has dropped by for a visit. She says she has a confession. Maybe she is pregnant. I had no idea that she was seeing anyone. That is such an odd locution. "Seeing" someone I thought would be the least of it. Molly will be happy to see her. Molly loves Anne. I think Molly loves me too but with reservations. I have to apply some discipline. Take the matter of the tennis shoes. I have an almost brand new pair. Molly decided that she wanted to chew on them. I took them away and hid them and replaced them by some rubber bones. Molly will not chew on the bones. Finally, I found an old pair of slippers which she agreed to chew on, but I think she resents the fact that I took away the tennis shoes.

Anne is wearing a wool skirt the color of an autumn leaf. She looks quite beautiful. I should tell her that she looks beautiful, but I am not sure that that is in our domain of discourse. Molly jumps up on the couch where Anne is sitting and puts her head in Anne's lap. Anne strokes her head in that magic way women have. Their fingers absorb pain. I remember that once I was in the hospital for a procedure that was quite painful but not painful enough to require an anesthetic. A nurse whom I could not see because I was on my stomach put her arm on by back. I could feel the pain being absorbed, I think that this is an evolutionary trait. The ones who could not do this lost their children. In any case, Molly looks very happy. Once in a while she glances at me as if to say "You see."

Anne confesses, "I have given up reading Wittgenstein. He makes no sense to me. I have no idea what you people see in him. His stuff is what you would find in a Chinese fortune cookie." "The last thing I found in a Chinese fortune cookie was 'Ignore the previous fortune'." I answer and then add, "I look at the *Tractatus* as a form of literature like *Finnegans Wake*. I don't expect to understand all of *Finnegans Wake* but every once in a while I stumble over a jewel such as '...they were yung and easily freudened...' Only a genius could come up with something like that. Wittgenstein was trying to figure out how language works. There is his example of a phrase in which every word makes sense but not the phrase. 'Socrates is identical.' What has gone wrong?"

"Suppose 'Socrates' and 'identical' were the names of cats", Anne says, "Then the sentence makes perfect sense." I reply weakly "If Wittgenstein wanted 'identical' to be the name of cat he would have put the 'i' in capital letters." "I am taking Molly for a walk," says Anne. "When you get back I will tell you about Gödel. I can assure that you will not find *him* in a fortune cookie."

V

I will begin my discussion with Anne when she gets back with a sketch of Gödel's life. He was born in what is now called Brno then part of the Austro-Hungarian empire in 1906. This makes him some six years younger than Wittgenstein. I wish I knew what his first mathematical memories were. Gödel was an obsessive collector of personal data. For example, he seems to have kept the library cards for every book he took out during most of his life. He kept a piece of paper on which he practiced subtraction when he was first learning it, things like $4 - 3 = 1$. I was hoping I might find a mistake but no such luck. There is an entry where he writes "$4 - 1 = 4$," but he crosses it out. When he was eighteen he entered the University of Vienna and studied physics for two years. But then he took a course in the theory of numbers and fell in love with it. His fellow students recall that he was always helpful when they got stuck, he was able to sort them out.

During his student days in Vienna, he shared apartments with his older brother Rudolf who was studying to be a doctor. The apartments, which they changed a good deal, were always large enough so as to accommodate visits from their recently widowed mother. For sixteen months, they lived at 72/14 Langegasse. Across the street at 65, lived a portrait photographer named Porkert. The oldest of his three daughters was named Adele Thusnelda Porkert. She had been married and divorced and was some six years older than Gödel. It is sometimes said that she had some sort of facial disfiguration, but the one photo I have seen taken in the 1930s shows an attractive blonde woman. Perhaps it shows her good side. Her profession is a bit murky. When Gödel met her she was a dancer working in a nightclub. She later said that she was a ballet dancer of which there is no evidence. In short, she was the kind of woman to give mothers a nightmare. Sex is a funny thing. Your mother may not have the last word.

I had an eye doctor once. He was, when I knew him, an elderly Jewish man who had been born in Poland. His mother tongue was Yiddish. Polish was a second language and English a third. He had gotten out of Poland just before it was taken over by the Germans. He lost most of his family. He had some relatives here and they took him in. He was a very bright boy and got through the university and medical school on scholarships. He was a wonderful doctor whose English was tinctured by Yiddish. One day I was in for a checkup. Clearly something was the matter — with him. He looked like a broken man. I was not going to say anything when suddenly he said "Sidney is going to marry a shiksa." I knew that his son Sidney was the apple of his eye. He had spent a lot of his savings to get Sidney through Harvard and medical school where he had studied to be an eye doctor like his father. Sidney was a real American who played baseball. At Harvard, he was surrounded by Protestants and that he would fall in love with one of them was entirely predictable. His mother, my doctor's wife had died, and now he had to bear the burden of this disgrace alone. I had no idea what to say to comfort the old man. It was beyond any Jewish joke I could think of. Finally, he said to me, "Now I vill make you ha muscle test." This involved putting some drops in my eyes so that my pupils would dilate like those of an ocelot. As he was doing this, he said to me, "Ven de schmekel rises up reason flies out de vindow."

Here is a missionary hymn that I like. It is called "From Greenland's Icy Mountains"

What though the spicy breezes
Blow soft o'er Ceylon's isle:
Though ev'ry prospect pleases
And only man is vile:
In vain with lavish kindness
The gifts of God are strown:
The heathen in his blindness
Bows down to wood and stone

Words by Reginald Heber (1819) and
music by Lowell Mason (1824)

Sometimes when I read about Gödel, to say nothing of my eye doctor's son, I wonder if sex is absolutely necessary. Even the Bible puts it off for a few days after the Creation. The original life forms were certainly not sexual. They were more like self-replicating automata. Sex only showed up as an afterthought, but once it caught on, it proved impossible to get rid of. There are animals that can do without it. Some kinds of lizards reproduce parthenogenetically. There are only females and, periodically, they produce eggs that hatch into clones of themselves — identical sisters. I am told that the biologists — male — who made this discovery went out in a group to the nearest bar and got soused. They felt threatened. But look on the bright side. Just think of all the time one could save without sex. It is true that there would be no Italian operas but still — the problem is, to use the term of art, that this is not an evolutionarily stable strategy.

Suppose there was a parasite that was fatal to these lizards. It could happen that there was a genetic mutation that rendered it harmless. One of the moms might acquire it and then pass it on to all her clone daughters. This would be good for them but everybody else would croak. The species would be very unlikely to survive. But lizards are not easy to dispense with, so some of the species change their sex spontaneously at least for a while. This propagates the gene pool, but I can imagine it leads to some confusion. I imagine the moms with their daughters going to a nice leafy place for a picnic. But then half the moms turn into dads. What was going to be a pleasant outing becomes something like a sailors' shore leave. The "dads" explain that they are only doing it for the good of the species. The moms say that they have heard that one before. It is puzzling that once these lizards have discovered sex they don't simply keep it like the rest of us. But I digress.

**VI**

After their father's death at age 54 in 1929, the brothers were left a sizable inheritance. Rudolf used some of his to travel while Gödel used some of his to get his own apartment. Adele was *persona non grata* in the Gödel family. It is not clear when Adele and Gödel began living together. In 1933, he made the first of his visits to Princeton where he spent the academic year at the Institute for Advanced Study. Adele did not go along. One has the impression that Gödel was not very happy that year. *Where every prospect pleases and only man is vile.* But the real problem was that there were no women. He was, as he later admitted, very frustrated sexually.

When he came back to Vienna in 1934, he had a nervous breakdown and entered a sanitarium. He recovered enough for a while to continue working. He made another trip by himself in the fall of 1935 to Princeton and had another nervous collapse and had to return to Vienna. At that point, Adele took over. There is a hotel receipt where she is registered as Frau Dr. Gödel.

Adele was a practical, intelligent person without much formal education. It is unlikely that she had the slightest idea of what Gödel had accomplished. Her role was to keep him viable. This was not easy. The borders between psychosomatic symptoms and the real thing are not always clearly demarcated. You can give yourself an ulcer by worrying too much that your son is going to marry a shiksa. Gödel had had digestive problems. He was persuaded that he was being poisoned. Once Adele took over, she tasted all his food before he ate it. This worked reasonably well so long as she was able to do it. But on July of 1977, she went into the hospital for major surgery. She could not return home until December. She found Gödel emaciated and persuaded him to go into the hospital. It was too late. When he died on January 14, 1978, he weighed sixty-five pounds.

When Gödel was still a student in Vienna, he had become an Austrian citizen. After the *Anschluss* in 1938, he became a German citizen, which made him eligible for the army. Gödel's feelings about leaving Austria were ambiguous. Neither he nor Adele had any Jewish ancestry. It is true that many of Gödel's teachers and colleagues including his thesis supervisor Hans Hahn were Jewish. Hahn had died in 1934, but many of the others had emigrated. Some of Gödel's mixed feelings became clear when he and Adele bought a new apartment in Vienna. Part of the problem was that he did not have a definite professorial offer from the Institute, which complicated his visa situation both to leave Germany and enter the United States. The matter was decided in 1939. He and Adele were walking near the university, and he was attacked by some young

Nazi thugs. Whether they mistook him for a Jew or knew that his thesis advisor was Jewish is not clear. They roughed Gödel up and knocked off his glasses. Adele attacked them with her umbrella and drove them off. This persuaded them to leave Austria.

The new director of the Institute, Frank Aydelotte, took matters into his hands. He wrote a strong letter to the German consul in Washington as well as the State Department. They issued non-quota emigration visas to Adele and Gödel. The Germans issued exit visas but on the condition that they exit through Russia. It appears that they did not want the Germans crossing the Atlantic where they might be captured by the English. The Gödels crossed the Lithuanian border on January 16, 1940. It took until February 2nd before they arrived in Yokohama, Japan, having crossed Russia on the trans-Siberian railroad. The boat they had planned to leave on for San Francisco had already left, but they did leave on the *President Cleveland* which arrived in San Francisco on March 4th. They took the train across the United States, a trip which Gödel apparently enjoyed. It took them about a week before they arrived in Princeton. Gödel was forty-eight, and he spent the last three decades of his life there.

## VII

"'You know Gödel has really gone crazy.' So I said, 'Well, what worse could he have done?' 'He voted for Eisenhower.'"

Einstein to his assistant Ernst Straus

Adele did not like Princeton. She referred to the Institute as an *Altersversorgungsheim* — a home for old age pensioners. Not only did every prospect not please but as far as she was concerned the inhabitants were vile. In some cases, the feelings were mutual. There was a very distinguished economist at the university named Oskar Morgenstern. He had been born in Germany but grew up in Vienna, where he held an important post. In 1938, he was visiting Princeton at the time of the *Anschluss.* It was clear that he could not go back, and Princeton offered him a professorship. He had known Gödel from Vienna and was one of the first to visit him in his first Princeton apartment. He seemed not to have met Adele before, and his judgment was very unflattering. He saw her as a "Viennese washerwoman type: garrulous, uncultured, [and] strong-willed." One imagines that it was a relief for Adele to find someone to talk to especially in German. Gödel was not very communicative. When Morgenstern asked about the present state of Vienna, Gödel told him that the coffee was bad.

Morgenstern did understand that Gödel's emotional life raft was being kept afloat by Adele. He may not have known the full extent of Gödel's paranoia. By this time, Gödel believed that the refrigerator and the radiators were emitting poison gas. For that reason, it was necessary to keep all the windows open and to remove the screens so as to allow the air to circulate more freely. A visiting neighbor reported about the insects. Adele was able to visit Vienna in 1947. Her mother had survived the war as had Gödel's mother and brother. She stayed away for seven months. Morganstern, who was then unmarried, tried to look after Gödel. They frequently had dinner together, and he ate enough so that when Adele returned while he was underweight, it was not catastrophic. After living in a few rented apartments, they bought a house and Adele put her energy into fixing it up. She had a fetish for chandeliers.

The strangest thing about Gödel's Institute years was his friendship with Einstein who once said that the best thing about the Institute was the chance to talk with Gödel. No two people could have been more different. Einstein never went to the Institute wearing a tie, and Gödel never went without one. Einstein loved Jewish jokes, especially if they were a little off-color. It is difficult to imagine Gödel telling a joke, although he did like Walt Disney movies such as *Snow White*. Furthermore, Einstein never had any interest in pure mathematics unless it had applications in physics. When he was a young man, Einstein had decided that his mathematical intuition was not strong enough to enable him to choose the really important problems, whereas in physics he had no trouble doing so. But he understood that Gödel had chosen a very small number of extremely important problems and could focus on them for years. In the voluminous Gödel *Nachlass* is a list he gave of all his technical published papers between the years 1930 and 1969. There were seventeen. Some he denoted by w — *wichtig* — important. There were five, and each changed the nature of mathematics.

I know that Anne will find Gödel interesting as a personality, but I want to convey more. I want to explain what he did but in such a way that she will get an understanding of how profound it was. I am starting to dream about Gödel. Last night, I had a dream in which there was a large reception.

It was hosted by Einstein and Gödel was the guest of honor. There was a reception line, and when I reached them, Einstein introduced us. Gödel said, "I knew your father in Vienna." I explained that my father had never been in Vienna. Gödel said again, "I knew your father in Vienna." I could see that it was hopeless. Einstein looked on amused.

## VIII

*Unentscheidbare* — undecidable — adj.
"He [von Neumann] under Hilbert's tutelage was trying to prove the opposite of Gödel's theorem. He worked and worked and worked at this and one night he dreamed the proof. He got up and wrote it down, and he got very close to the end. He went and worked all day on this part, and the next night he dreamed again. He dreamed how to close the gap, and he got up and wrote and got within epsilon of the end, but he couldn't make the final step. So he went to bed. The next day he worked and worked and worked at it, and he said to me, 'You know, it was very lucky Herman, that I didn't dream the third night, or think what state mathematics would be in today'" [Laughter]

Herman Goldstine 4.121

"Propositions cannot represent the logical form: this mirrors itself in propositions.
That which mirrors itself in language, language cannot represent.
That which represents *itself* in language, *we* cannot express by language."

*Tractatus* by Wittgenstein

When he was still a doctoral student, Gödel was invited probably by his thesis advisor Hans Hahn to join the Vienna Circle. In their coffee shop meetings, they were engaged in trying to purge physics and mathematics and everything else from the metaphysics of people like Kant. The group called themselves "logical positivists" — whatever that meant. When Gödel joined, they were studying the *Tractatus*. Wittgenstein was a member — sort of.

In the occasional meetings he attended, he said nothing and read poetry. Perhaps the most influential figure in the group was Rudolf Carnap. He was somewhat older than Gödel and had been born in Germany. He had studied physics at the University of Berlin where Einstein was then a professor. By 1926, he had gotten a professorship at the University of Vienna. One of his philosophical points was that mathematics was merely a "syntax of language." Putting things in a wildly anachronistic way, all the truths of mathematics could be found by programming a computer to generate proofs. If any proof could be found this way in a finite time, you would know everything there is to be known about whatever mathematical system — say number theory — that you were interested in. What Gödel was in the process of doing was showing that there were mathematical truths that could not be found this way. Indeed, the truth or falsity of such propositions was undecidable — *unentscheidbare* — and indeed among these undecidable propositions was the consistency of the system itself. If you believe this, then you are led to believe that there are mathematical truths that are beyond proof. Gödel became a Platonist with the belief that there was just such a mathematical realm. This led him to stop going to the Vienna Circle meetings, although he did retain an admiration for Carnap. When things got bad in Germany, Carnap emigrated to the United States in 1935 and became a citizen in 1941. He held various positions in universities here and spent some time at the Institute — where he renewed his friendship with Gödel — until finally ending up at UCLA. This is mere biographical distraction. Now, I have to face up to the task of explaining Gödel.

The first of the great *unentscheidbare* papers was published in 1931. I have to confess that I have never read it from the beginning till the end. It is too hard. But I think I can explain the basic ideas to Anne since I have read a great deal about it. It will be, if can put it this way, a case of the myopic leading the blind. The goal of Gödel's paper is to produce a proposition in a suitably rich logical structure which says of itself that it is not provable. This kind of self-referential paradox has a long history beginning with the "liar". Suppose I come across a message that says "This message is false,"

I am immediately in a cleft stick. If it is true it is false, and if it is false then it is true. We see that this paradox contains a whole implicit linguistic structure behind it. The statement "This message is silly" might be silly, but it is certainly not paradoxical.

I have decided that at this point in my lecture to Anne we will need a pause. I have bought an excellent bottle of Nuits-Saint-Georges and some *amuse bouches* from the French boutique down the street. Molly will be given some treats. Then we will be ready for the heavy lifting.

The first thing that I will explain to Anne is that Gödel's results require dealing with a system that is rich enough to contain all of arithmetic — not just addition and subtraction. If all you care about is addition and subtraction, it can be shown that the system is complete and consistent. Russell's question "Are we to think that 2+2 is not 4 but 4.01?" is total nonsense. There was a rich system that Gödel took as a prototype. He made it clear that it was only one example. Bertrand Russell and Alfred North Whitehead took on the task of reducing all of mathematics to symbolic logic. This was a logic with a few axioms and rules of deduction which combined symbols to prove propositions. They succeeded in doing this for arithmetic, and they published the results in their monumental *Principia Mathematica*. There was a second edition in 1927, and this is what Gödel used. They never got farther than arithmetic because as Russell said they ran out of energy. It might also be said that Gödel's work made the whole thing seem a bit pointless.

To begin my explanation, I am going to translate the statement, "Not (not vanilla and not chocolate)" — which means the same thing as "vanilla or chocolate" — into symbols. I do not have to use the whole array of symbols for this. Here are the ones I do have to use. I will explain the numbers shortly.

| ~ | not | 1 |
|---|---|---|
| ( | left parens | 2 |
| ) | right parens | 3 |
| . | and | 4 |

| = | equal | 5 |
|---|-------|---|
| v | or    | 6 |

This set of symbols is nice because they are on the standard keyboard. I will call "vanilla" *p* and "chocolate" *q*. Here is the translation

$$\sim(\sim p \ . \ \sim q) = (p \ \text{v} \ q)$$

The next step Gödel took was to replace such propositions by a number. It is called a Gödel number but the way he did it with prime numbers is much more sophisticated than what I am going to do. The advantage of his way is that by examining a number you can decide whether it is or is not the Gödel number of some proposition. I will just use the table above and will call *p* — "7" and *q* — "8". Thus, $\sim(\sim p \ . \ \sim q) = (p \ \text{v} \ q)$ becomes 1274183427683. Why bother with this? This coding will enable the system to make statements about itself, and we are now alert to knowing that when this happens paradoxes are lurking.

To say a proposition is "provable" in our system is to say given the axioms and the rules of deduction we can write out a string of symbols that imply the proposition. To say it is "unprovable" is to say there is no such string. To say it is "undecidable" is to say we have no way of knowing if there is or there is not such a string. What Gödel did was to construct an example in the Russell Whitehead logic of a proposition that is undecidable. The fact that we have a proposition for which we have not yet found a proof might mean that it is undecidable or it might mean that we are being stupid. In the introduction to his paper, Gödel gave a simplified version of his argument. This is what I am going try to explain to Anne.

A string of symbols with a Gödel number *x* may or may not be a proof of a proposition with Gödel number *g*. If it is, we designate this symbolically with Prf(*g:x*). If it is not, we write ~Prf(*g:x*]. If there are no *x*'s which are proofs of *g*, then the proposition is unprovable. In symbolic logic, "all" is represented by ∀, an inverted 'A'. Thus, the statement of the unprovability of $g$ is given symbolically by $\forall x \sim \text{Prf}(g{:}x)$. But this proposition has a Gödel number $G$. We can substitute $G$ for $g$ arriving at $\forall x \sim \text{Prf}(G{:}x)$. This statement has the Gödel number $\hat{G}$. But this statement, which is provable, says that $\hat{G}$ is not provable. We have constructed a statement which has the property that both the statement and its negative are provable. But this is not possible in a consistent theory. The only way out is to say that the provability or unprovability of this statement is undecidable — *unentscheidbare*. In short, there are statements in arithmetic, for example, which are unprovable even though possibly true. But there was more. In a subsequent paper, Gödel showed that one of these unprovable statements was the consistency of the system itself. We cannot prove that the system that is rich enough to contain arithmetic is consistent with itself.

In late August of 1930, Gödel met Carnap in a café and told him about the first of his results. The consistency argument had not yet been formulated. How much Carnap understood is not clear, but he said that Gödel should give a talk about it at a conference on the *Epistemology of the Exact Sciences*, which was going to be held in Königsberg in East Prussia a few days later. Königsberg was the birthplace of Immanuel Kant. Indeed, he spent his whole life there. Gödel had read Kant and had decided that he disagreed with Kant's view of mathematical truths. These truths were not objective but reflected the structure of our minds. As I have mentioned, when it came to mathematics, Gödel was a Platonist. There was a realm of mathematical truth which had an objective reality. It is odd that Gödel did come to agree with Kant's notion of time. There is no such thing as objective time, but it is our subjective way of ordering events. This he felt was the lesson of Einstein's theory of relativity in which each observer has his or her proper time. What is remarkable was that in the 1940s he invented a cosmology based on Einstein's general theory of relativity, which embodied these notions. It is an odd cosmology in which travel backward in time is possible if you expend enough energy. It requires an expanding universe that rotates which ours does not. Einstein was very intrigued by Gödel's invention.

There were mathematicians at the Königsberg conference. One of them was David Hilbert, a German mathematician who many people think was the greatest of his era. Hilbert gave a keynote address in which he urged his fellow mathematicians to carry out a program which would show the completeness and consistency of arithmetic. He was quite unaware that Gödel was in the process of showing that this program was impossible and indeed had already established the incompleteness part. Gödel gave a sort of side talk. The only person who understood what Gödel was saying was John von Neumann. Ironically, he had had a fellowship to study under Hilbert in Gottingen in 1926–1927. Indeed, he had tried to carry out Hilbert's program, which he now realized was impossible. Von Neumann proved that Gödel's result implied that the consistency of the system was undecidable. He did not publish because Gödel had gotten the result. But he became a great admirer of Gödel and when he became a Professor at The Institute for Advanced Study, he used his influence to get Gödel invited as a visitor and finally as a permanent member.

This is what I plan to tell Anne. In preparation, I have made a large notice printed in ink which reads "This notice is false." I have taped it to my door.

## IX

Anne comes back with Molly. Molly immediately heads for the kitchen where she knows her supper will be ready. As Anne takes off her jacket, she says to me, "I met your friend Elena. I think she is lovely." "Stop!" "Just stop!" I shout. I shout so loudly that poor Molly comes running from the kitchen and climbs into Anne's lap for comfort. "What is the matter with you?" Anne asks. "That you of all people would ask that," I answer, "is incredible." You have told me ever since we got to know each other that when I get anywhere near any women I should wear a poison warning around my neck and now you are trying to fix me up. "What is the matter with you?" I have that rising panic feeling like those convicts in Britain who were sentenced to spend the rest of their lives in a penal colony in Australia beginning with a three-month hazardous trip by sailboat.

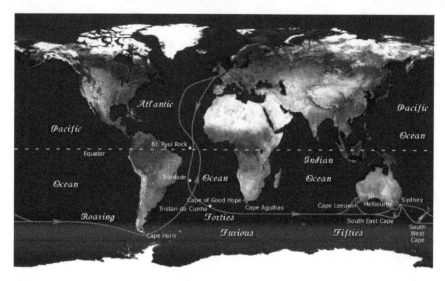

"I am not trying to do anything," Anne protests. "She seems like she would be a nice friend for you to have and the two dogs get on so well. I tell you what I will do. I will come over and make dinner for the three of us. The two dogs can have supper together and afterwards I will take her home. You will be fine."

This has come to pass. Elena is in the living room while Anne is cooking dinner. I am not sure what to say to her. She starts the conversation. "Anne tells me that you are going to tell her about Gödel," "Yes," I say condescendingly, "Do you know of him?" "I was wondering," Elena says, "whether you were going to tell her only about the *unentscheidbare* papers or also about the ones on the continuum hypothesis."

# Chapter 3

"Until a more precise analysis of the statements of quantum mechanics will enable us to prove objectively the possibility of hidden parameters we shall abandon this possible explanation. We therefore adopt the opposite point of view. That is, we admit as a fact that those natural laws that govern the elementary processes (i.e., the laws of quantum mechanics) are of a statistical nature."

John von Neumann
*Mathematical Foundations of Quantum Mechanics*, p. 210

"Well one day I was at the Institute for Advanced Study, and I went to Gödel's office, and there was Gödel. It was winter and Gödel had an electric heater and had his legs wrapped in a blanket. I said, 'Professor Gödel, what connection do you see between your incompleteness theorem and Heisenberg's uncertainty principle'. And Gödel got angry and threw me out of his office."

John Wheeler

"Gödel proved that the world of pure mathematics is inexhaustible; no finite set of axioms and rules of inference can ever encompass the whole of mathematics; given any set of axioms, we can find meaningful mathematical questions which the axioms leave unanswered. I hope that an analogous situation exists in the physical world. If my view of the future is correct, it means that the world of physics and astronomy is also inexhaustible; no matter how far we go into the future, there will always be new things happening, new information coming in, new worlds to explore, a constantly expanding domain of life, consciousness and memory."

Freeman Dyson

I

In a manner of speaking, the Institute for Advanced Study opened its doors in the fall of 1933. In a manner of speaking, because the Institute did not have any doors to open. The School of Mathematics, in which Einstein and von Neumann were professors, had its offices on the Princeton University campus in Fine Hall where the offices of the Princeton mathematics faculty had its offices. In the mid-1930s, Einstein was informed that some experiment had shown that his theory of relativity which had been making correct predictions since 1905 was wrong. He commented *Raffiniert ist der Herrgott, aber boshaft ist er nicht* — God is sophisticated but not malicious. This was engraved above the fireplace in the common room in Fine Hall. Needless to say, the experiments were wrong.

In 1932, von Neumann had published his *Mathematische Grundlagen der Quantenmechanik* — The Mathematical Foundations of Quantum Mechanics. For several previous years, physicists had been inventing or rediscovering their own mathematics. Now, von Neumann was going to make it all rigorous. There were axioms and lemmas and theorems and very little new physics. In 1933, he gave a series of lectures at the Institute on this. Gödel attended and so no doubt did Einstein. I imagine his attitude was *ein Affe in eine Kappe ist gerade noch ein Affe* — An ape in a cap is still only an ape.

His first reaction to the statistical nature of the theory was to remark that in his view, God did not play dice with the world. Then he tried for a few years to show that the theory was wrong. When this didn't succeed, he tried to show that the theory did not describe all of reality. Indeed, at about the time of von Neumann's lectures, Einstein began work with two junior colleagues, Nathan Rosen and Boris Podolsky, to create a thought experiment that demonstrated this. Meanwhile, quantum mechanics was going from strength to strength so no one paid much attention. Later, Gödel came to agree with Einstein; John Wheeler who was a Physics Professor at Princeton said that Gödel had been "brainwashed." Von Neumann's rigorous mathematics must have seemed to Einstein like a monumental waste of time.

Speaking of time wasted, you must be wondering why this man is banging on about the quantum theory when we left Elena asking about the *unentscheidbare* papers as well as the continuum hypothesis. When I heard this, the first thing that occurred to me was, what is the probability that a woman I had met casually in the park with her dog would know about these things? The future is always only probable. I believe the Sun will come up tomorrow but I could not give a rigorous proof. But this? I can understand how someone not involved in these things might have heard of Gödel. Perhaps through Alan Turing who translated Gödel's theorems into limitations on what can be programmed on an ideal computer. His life story ending with his suicide by eating a poisoned apple is the stuff of dramas. Still, knowing that the word *unentscheidbare* appears in the title of Gödel's first paper is not something you would learn if you saw a play about Turing. And the continuum hypothesis? But before I get into all this, I must tell you about a dream.

## II

In my dream I am going to the Moon on a Greyhound bus. It is being driven by Wittgenstein. He is wearing a yellow long-sleeved T-shirt with a picture on the front of Einstein and Gödel.

On the back, in large letters is "y-knot" with an image.

Wittgenstein reads *Gone with the Wind* during the trip. Molly is there of course. We spend the time on the trip doing crossword puzzles. She points out letters from a table and I write them in. We have a lot of trouble with "syzygy." The first "y" is tricky. We land on the shores of a lake. Anne is there and has prepared a picnic lunch. Doctor Levman is also there. He and Wittgenstein try to solve the riddle of what has a hooker, a looker, and two sticky wickys. Before lunch, Molly and I go for a swim. She has never been in the water before but takes to it at once. She is fascinated by the silver fish that swim around next to her. We all hate to leave the Moon but we have things to do.

III

Georg Cantor was born in St. Petersburg in 1845. His father was a fairly well-to-do businessman. This was fortunate because throughout his life Cantor was not dependent on his academic income — fortunate because until some years after he created it his mathematics was declared crazy if not degenerate. Like many very gifted mathematical people, he also had a great talent for music and could have become a professional violinist. When Cantor was eleven, the family moved to Germany because the Russian winters were too cold. He was largely educated in Germany, and after he got his PhD at the University of Berlin, he found his way to the University of Halle where he spent the rest of his life. The work that got him into trouble began in 1874. He began asking what does infinity mean? Before you raise your hand, here are some things to consider.

Unless we are mathematicians, we really do not have to deal with infinity. It is out there somewhere bigger than anything we do have to deal with. The number of anything we do have to deal with may be very large but we are sure that if we counted long enough we could attach a number to it. There is no limit to the size of these numbers. If you say that the integer $m$ is the biggest one, I will simply add 1 to it and get a bigger one, $m + 1$. But here is where the trouble begins. Take all the integers, both positive and negative. Clearly, there are in this sense an infinite number of them. But let us take only the positive integers. There are clearly an infinite number of them. But they are half the number of all the integers including the negative ones. This is a paradox of the infinite. The size of a set of objects is called its "cardinal number." The cardinal number of the set of all positive integers is the same as the set of all even numbers, which is the same as the set of all odd integers. It is also the same as the set of all ratios of integers. More tricky is the set of all prime numbers, integers which are only divisible by themselves and one. "Euclid," which I think was short for some ancient Greek Institute for Advanced Study, showed the number of these was the same as the number of integers. Cantor used the Hebrew aleph with a subscript zero to designate that number.

The aleph was the Kabalic symbol for the infinite mystery and domain of God. Next, Cantor raised the question of whether there were infinities that were larger than aleph zero. Here is where he began to get into trouble with the authorities.

This had happened before. Hippasus of Metapontum, a 5th century BC Pythagorean, was said to have discovered that the square root of two could not be represented as the ratio of integers while he was on a boat sailing with other Pythagoreans. His fellow Pythagoreans, who thought that everything involved integers, were so upset that they dumped him overboard and left him to drown. That didn't help, and it was soon shown that most square roots could not be expressed as the ratio of integers. Then prior to Cantor, it was shown that certain logarithms and pi itself could not be expressed this way. But Cantor was the first one to ask what this meant about the number of such numbers. Was it the same as the number of integers or larger? Cantor's proof that it was larger is so simple that one finds incomprehensible as to why it got him into such trouble. It depends on the fact that all these numbers can be expressed as a series of decimals. Take pi for example. The first one hundred and one terms in the expansion are given by

3.14159 26535 89793 23846 26433 83279 50288 41971 69399 37510
58209 74944 59230 78164 06286 20899 86280 34825 34211 70679 ...

The three dots mean that the series, which never repeats itself, continues forever. What Cantor imagined was that all such series could be lined up in a countable way.

$$
\begin{aligned}
E_0 &= m\ m\ m\ m\ m\ m\ m\ m\ m\ m\ m\ m\ \cdots \\
E_1 &= w\ w\ w\ w\ w\ w\ w\ w\ w\ w\ w\ w\ \cdots \\
E_2 &= m\ w\ m\ w\ m\ w\ m\ w\ m\ w\ m\ w\ \cdots \\
E_3 &= w\ m\ w\ m\ w\ m\ w\ m\ w\ m\ m\ w\ \cdots \\
E_4 &= w\ m\ m\ w\ w\ m\ m\ w\ m\ w\ m\ w\ \cdots \\
E_5 &= m\ w\ m\ w\ w\ m\ w\ m\ w\ m\ w\ m\ \cdots \\
E_6 &= m\ w\ m\ w\ w\ m\ w\ w\ m\ w\ m\ w\ \cdots \\
E_7 &= w\ m\ m\ w\ m\ w\ m\ w\ m\ w\ m\ w\ \cdots \\
E_8 &= m\ m\ w\ m\ w\ m\ w\ m\ w\ m\ w\ m\ \cdots \\
E_9 &= w\ m\ w\ m\ m\ w\ w\ m\ w\ w\ m\ w\ \cdots \\
E_{10} &= w\ w\ m\ w\ m\ w\ m\ w\ m\ m\ w\ m\ \cdots \\
E_{11} &= m\ w\ m\ w\ w\ m\ w\ m\ m\ w\ m\ m\ \cdots \\
&\ \vdots \\
E_u &= w\ m\ w\ w\ m\ w\ m\ m\ m\ m\ m\ w\ \cdots
\end{aligned}
$$

Now all you have to do to get a number which is not on the list is change the first digit in the first number, the second digit in the second number, and so on down the diagonal. The number that results is nowhere to be found on the list. Hence, the set of these numbers must have larger cardinality than $\aleph_0$. He called it $\aleph_1$. Some of the people who objected to his line of reasoning had a point. Cantor had not really constructed the missing number. To do so, you would have to carry out the diagonalization to infinity. Most mathematicians accept Cantor's argument.

Cantor made a conjecture. There is no infinity between $\aleph_0$ and $\aleph_1$. This became known as the "continuum hypothesis." Between any two ordinary numbers, there is always a third with a value somewhere in between. Hence, these numbers form a "continuum" and $\aleph_1$ is the number of the numbers that make it up. He spent much of the rest of his career trying unsuccessfully to prove it. It is sometimes said that his failure along with the criticism of his work in general pushed him into such a state of depression that from time to time he had to be institutionalized. He died in a mental institution in 1918.

Gödel must have known many branches of mathematics but he published in very few. He worked on the continuum hypothesis for twenty years. He seemed to have wavering ideas as to whether or not it was even true. When one talks of "proof," one must specify the rules of the game. There is a standard set of axioms that are assumed. It was this set of axioms that Gödel used. In 1940, Gödel showed that the continuum hypothesis was consistent with these axioms. This is a far cry from proving it. Here is where things stood until the early 1960s. There then appeared some very unexpected work by a young mathematician named Paul Cohen then at Stanford University. Up to that time, Cohen had not had much interest in the foundations of mathematics. This was fortunate because he was not steeped in techniques that did not work. But he found a new technique which enabled him to show that within the context of these axioms you could not prove the falsity of the continuum hypothesis. As far as these axioms were concerned, putting Gödel and Cohen together showed that the continuum hypothesis was not decidable. Cohen was very uneasy about this and felt that he had to show the work to Gödel so in the spring of 1963 he went to Princeton to find Gödel.

There is some irony in this since Cohen had spent two years — 1959–1961 — at the Institute and had no interest in Gödel's work. When he got to Princeton in 1963, Gödel was in one of his reclusive phases and did not often come to his office. Einstein had died in 1955, so his one close contact with the Institute was no longer there. But Cohen looked him up in his house. Gödel was willing to see him and Cohen gave him what amounted to a first draft of his manuscript. He was delighted to receive a letter from Gödel in which he wrote,

"Let me repeat that it is really a delight to read your proof of the independence of the continuum hypothesis. I think that in all essential respects you have given the best possible proof and this does not happen frequently. Reading your proof had a similarly pleasant effect on me as seeing a really good play."

One can only wonder what plays Gödel was talking about and where he saw them. Gödel volunteered to prepare the manuscript for publication. Cohen agreed and then had to endure months while Gödel dotted every "I" and crossed every "t." On his next stint at the Institute, Gödel was happy to talk with him but at intervals of every two weeks for an hour. Cohen found him physically and mentally fragile. Cohen who received every possible honor that the mathematics community could award, died in 2007 at the age of 72. But I have digressed from Elena and probabilities.

The quantum theory conditions us to think probabilistically. How probable is any sequence of events? How probable is it to find an elegant woman in the park with a dog about the same age as Molly who has heard of the continuum hypothesis. Let us break things up. First how probable is it to find an elegant woman in the park with a dog? I have concluded that it is highly probable. Women, and indeed men, go into the park to meet each other. A dog is an objective correlative. This has been recognized by Paws who rent out dogs by the day for people who would like to take them to the park. As I look around when I am in the park, I am sure many of the dogs I see have been rented. It would be a little awkward if two people who rented dogs returned them to Paws at the same time. It would also be awkward if you showed up on different days with different dogs rented from Paws. I am quite sure that Elena's dog Stanley has not been rented from Paws. It is of course less probable that her dog would be about the same age and size as Molly. If the dog had been a Great Dane, I would have been concerned.

Most people are not entirely at ease with the abstract. Think about it. Spoken language is learned instinctively but written language must be taught. Writing is one of the first abstractions we learn — transferring sound into symbols. Arithmetic comes at about the same time. This is a real abstraction. Anne is certainly a very intelligent person, but she had a hard time learning to add. She could add two oranges to two oranges to get four oranges or two apples to two apples to get four apples, but when she was asked to add two oranges to two apples she got stuck. Four of what? Subtraction was even worse. How do you subtract two apples from two oranges? I would imagine Gödel had no problem. Here is a table written as a child.

There is a little slip at the top, but he has caught it. He must have loved these numbers. Nothing is more abstract than symbolic logic. It was for him as natural as breathing. The chance of finding someone like Elena in the park borders on the infinitesimal. I am trying to form a tactful question when Anne comes out of the kitchen. She does not trust me to tidy up anything. She says, "I am going to walk Elena home." Just before she closes the door to my apartment, she gives me a wink.

## IV

I have had another dream about going to the Moon in a Greyhound bus. Wittgenstein is again driving. He is again wearing a yellow long-sleeved T-shirt. On the front is the last proposition in the *Tractatus* in German — *Wovon man nicht sprechen kann, darüber muss man schweigen* — Whereof one cannot speak, thereof one must be silent. On the back in a large symbol is $\aleph_1$. Wittgenstein is reading *The Catcher in the Rye*. Gödel wearing a jacket and tie is there. He is ignoring Wittgenstein by listening to Miles Davis on his iPod. Molly and I work on crossword puzzles. We are stuck on the word 'adjugate'. Is it a noun or a verb or something else? We land at the same lake. Anne is there and so are Elena and Stanley. He and Molly jump into the lake and try to catch the silvery fish. Elena and Anne have set up a tent. Gödel goes inside to keep out of the Sun. Anne and Elena have made us a wonderful lunch. Gödel tells us the first time he went to the Sacher Hotel in Vienna for the Sacher Torte.

They are all numbered. "My number was 87539319. It is the smallest number than can be written as the sum of cubes of positive integers in three different ways. $167^3 + 436^3 = 228^3 + 423^3 = 255^3 + 414^3$."

## V

I have had another dream. I would ask Doctor Levman about it, but he is an important part of it. Maybe this recuses him. I will find out. In my dream, Doctor Levman has taken Anne and me prisoner. We are kept in separate cells and cannot communicate, but Doctor Levman can make visits to us. On his first visit to me he says that I have two choices, to confess or deny. To what, he does not explain. He then tells me the possibilities. If I confess and Anne denies, I will serve two and a third years and she will go free. If I deny and she confesses, then I will go free and she will serve for two and a third years. If I confess and she confesses, we will serve for only a day as a reward for our honesty. If we both deny, we will both serve ten days. He tells me that he has made the same offer to Anne. He gives me nineteen minutes to make up my mind.

Here is how I reason. Suppose she confesses. I have two choices, to confess or deny. If I confess I will serve for a day, but if I deny I will go free. So it is worth my while to deny. If Anne denies and I confess she will go free, and I will serve the two and a third years. If I deny we will serve for only ten days. Hence, no matter what she does, it is better for me to deny. But she will come to the same conclusion and hence we will both deny and serve for ten days. But this is not the best outcome. The best outcome is for us to both confess, but I can't take advantage of this with the knowledge I have since I must make assumptions about her behavior. Doctor Levman finds this dilemma very amusing. "I will write a paper about it," he says. "They will give me a prize," he adds. I am sure that there is something wrong here and I wake up with a headache.

## VI

I feel that I need to see Doctor Levman. I want to see if he can help me understand my dream. I call him and explain that he is part of the dream and so is Anne. Will that be a problem? He says that he does not think so. I am going to take Molly. I would like Doctor Levman to meet her and I don't want to leave Molly alone for a long time in the apartment. She always comes with me when I buy groceries or have a haircut. Molly has never been in an automobile so she is a little hesitant about getting into the taxi. I give her a treat and put her down in the seat next to me. Doctor Levman has said that I could bring her. Molly likes looking out the window of the taxi but seems quite willing to get out of the car when we arrive at the park near Doctor Levman's office. I have purposely come early so I can take Molly to the park. She seems intrigued and stakes a claim to various trees. There are new dogs to sniff. Then we go to Doctor Levman's office.

I sit in my usual chair and Molly goes to sleep on the rug. I tell Doctor Levman about my dream leaving out the part about him getting a prize. He wants to know why I assumed that Anne would choose "deny." "It is the most reasonable choice," I explain. "The heart has its reasons which reason cannot know," Doctor Levman says. "But any other choice would not have been reasonable," I say. I then begin to sob. Doctor Levman has seen this before. He says nothing. But Molly senses that something is wrong and gets onto my chair and puts her head in my lap. "She loves you," Doctor Levman says.

# Chapter 4

Michael Ventris with a detail from the Tripode tablet.

"Though it runs completely counter to everything I've said in the past I'm now almost completely convinced that the tablets are in GREEK."

Michael Ventris

"Man drew before he talked."

Sir Arthur Evans

I was a math major at Harvard. I was a good student and took all
the advanced courses. One of them was Quine's logic and mathematical
foundations. He invented a paradox.

"Yields a falsehood when appended to its own quotation."
Yields a falsehood when appended to its own quotation.
Wonderful.

Soon after I got my master's degree, two things happened. I realized
that I would never be able to create mathematics. I had studied the subject
for years and years and had never had an original thought. I was sure that
with help I could write a PhD thesis on a problem suggested by a teacher.
I was also sure that this would be the last bit of research I would do. I
would end up teaching in a small college or prep school. In some sense, my
intellectual life would be over. Just as I had this realization, something else
happened. I inherited a great deal of money from an uncle I hardly knew. He
had no family and neither did I. Put another way, we were the only family
we had. When I finally came to terms with my inheritance, I realized that
if I invested it sensibly and lived reasonably, I would never have to work
again. Then what?

The first thing I decided to do was to travel around the world. It took
two years. I lived in Paris for a while and audited courses at the Sorbonne.
I went bicycling on Crete and snorkeling in Bali. I went trekking in Nepal
and traveled in India — the Taj by moonlight. Sometimes I met a woman
who was traveling in the same direction or in no direction. We would travel
together for a while and then go our own ways. Since I had no address, I did
not expect to hear from her again. One morning in April in Kathmandu I
decided that I had had enough. It was the pre-monsoon season and it was
like living in a sauna. I was tired of suitcases and backpacks and suspect
water and food. I had had a couple of bouts with dysentery and was grateful
that it was nothing worse. I wanted to go home or at least create a home to
go back to. But where?

Cambridge would have been a possibility, but it was also a symbol of failure. All those years of study leading finally to nowhere. I suppose I could have gone to California, but it seemed too trendy so I chose New York. I decided that I would live in Greenwich Village near NYU. I was sure that there would be bookstores and probably some lectures I could go to. My idea was to spend different amounts of time learning about anything that caught my interest. I would become an intellectual vagabond. There were no curricula and no final exams. I took a room in a local hotel and began looking for an apartment I could buy. I wanted a quiet building where everything worked. I found one and then hired a decorator to fix up my apartment. I told her that I wanted wall-to-wall bookshelves. "How many books do you have?" she asked. "None," I said, "but there will be dozens and dozens." So when I finally moved into the place, there were empty bookshelves everywhere. It did not take long to begin filling them up. As a start, I got dictionaries in all sorts of languages. From my background, it was understandable that I was interested in the number systems in these languages. Take the number "five" in Greek "πέντε-pente" and the same number in Sanskrit "panch." Or the Greek for "three," "tria" and the Sanskrit "tri." Clearly, this is not an accident. This led me to William Jones. He was a jurist in British India at the end of the 18$^{th}$ century. He was also a linguistic genius. One of the many languages he learned was Sanskrit. He noted the deep connection between it and Greek and made the conjecture that they were both offshoots of a parent language, which was very likely no longer spoken. This began the study of Proto Indo European and of the people who for reasons still unknown migrated from the Central Asiatic steppes in the second millennium spreading their language. I soon had bookshelves filled with books about historical linguistics. The books also led me to Anne.

I found a bookstore that was perfect for me. It had three stories and they were all packed with books. If you wanted to study the quantum theory, for example, there were many shelves in all sorts of languages. If they didn't have the book, they would order it for you. I opened an account. I noticed a very attractive woman who worked there. She was always well-dressed and carefully put together. She was friendly but reserved. Her curiosity was aroused, and one day she asked me what I did. I told her that I was a professional dilettante. She wondered if I could earn a living that way. I told her that I did not need to earn a living since my father was a Saudi prince. We went for coffee and she asked what I really did. I told her that I was a dilettante who once studied mathematics. "Why did you stop?" she asked. "I wasn't good enough," I told her and then explained the part about creativity. "I would have tried to do a good job teaching," I explained. "Maybe when I retired my ex-students would have gotten together to buy me a watch with my name engraved on it." "Were you married?" she asked. "No," I answered. "Marriage is like a long dull dinner with the dessert at the beginning." "That was Oscar Wilde," she said. "He was just the person to consult about marriage." "Were you married?" I asked. "Yes," she said, "but I am not sure that we ever had dessert." "What happened?" I asked. "He dumped me because I was not evolving fast enough." "An odd locution," I answered. "It makes you sound like a bacterial colony in which a strange parasite has been introduced." "He kept moving up the legal food chain, and I was stuck in the kitchen cooking dinner." "Where is he now?" I asked. "He is in jail. He began investing his client's money without their permission and he was not very good at it. Fortunately enough was recovered so my alimony payments continue. But to keep myself in caviar and champagne I work."

We made a deal. She was not going to sleep with me or move in. "Been there and done that," she said. "After my divorce I thought I might enter a convent but I didn't like the hours. But I will do some homemaking for you. What are you eating?" "Stouffer's Chicken a la King," I answered. "We used to eat that kind of thing at debutante parties," she said. "It's a wonder that we survived. I will cook you some real food and in return you will take me along on these intellectual rocket ships you seem to go off on. I didn't learn much in college except how to find a man to marry and I flunked that course."

When Anne first looked at my kitchen, she was horrified. There was a microwave and a freezer full of frozen dinners. I had some bananas on top of the refrigerator, but they were past their prime. There was nothing to cook with and no proper utensils. "You give me a budget and then stay out of my way," she said. I told her to spend whatever she needed to. "I also don't like your shower curtains," she said. "All those fish. It looks like an aquarium."

"I never take a shower," I told her.

Over the next few days, Anne outfitted my kitchen. You could actually cook something there. She bought wine glasses and some candles. We had romantic dinners except that there was no romance. I told her about Wittgenstein and Gödel and about Einstein. I told her about William Jones and Proto Indo European. We discussed the quantum theory. She found some of it tough going, but she always came back for more. She never liked Wittgenstein. "He looked like an insurance salesman," she said improbably. I told her about Doctor Levman. "Except that you are crazy why are you going to him?" "He says it's about giving me more choices," I explained. "Now on the question of marriage I have no choice. It is simply not an option. Maybe I can make it an option even if I choose not to exercise it." "Beware of analysts bearing gifts," she commented. We listened to T. S. Eliot reciting "The Waste Land." "He sounds like he has a clothes pin on his nose," she noted. "He was born in St. Louis but when he moved to England he had to learn English," I explained.

I have no good way of explaining how I lit on a subject. I guess the choice of "Linear-B" was as logical as it is going to get. One night, I was showing Anne some of the pictures I had taken while bicycling on Crete. We came to one that caught her attention. "What is that?" she asked. "That's Knossos or at least what's left of it?" "Why?" she asked. I was not sure what she meant but it seemed like a good excuse to explore a bit of archeology. We had had enough of Gödel. "You are looking at the fruits of an obsession," I said, "the obsession of Arthur Evans."

Arthur Evans, I explained to her, came from one of those well-to-do English merchant families of the 19th century. His father Jack married his cousin Harriet. Her father owned a very successful paper mill and Jack became a partner in the business. He was an interesting man who collected Stone-Age artifacts and eventually was knighted by Queen Victoria. Young Evans went to Harrow and then to Oxford. He graduated with a First under somewhat dicey conditions. After graduation, he went abroad and ended up in the Balkans like some sort of Graham Greene character — an agent of some kind. He parlayed this into a job as a foreign correspondent for the *Manchester Guardian*. He always had an interest in archeology and got a job as Keeper of the Ashmolean Museum in Oxford.

First he did some digging in England and then he changed his *modus operandi* to the Continent. His beloved wife died and he wandered somewhat aimlessly digging in places like Zagreb. While he was at the Ashmolean, he had been given some seal stones from Crete. He was struck by the odd signs on them. When he and his wife were in Athens, he purchased some more and was then determined to go to Crete and study their source. After his wife's death, this became an obsession. The problem was that the site at which they had been discovered — Knossos — was the province of the German archeologist Heinrich Schliemann. Schliemann was famous for his discoveries of the buried cities of Homer's Troy which were located in what is now Turkey. He was planning to make a full-scale excavation of Knossos, but he died. The site was owned by two Moslem brothers, but after Schliemann's death, and the eviction of the Turks from the Island, Evans was able to buy it. By this time, he had seen more examples of the tablets and he had concluded that he was in the presence of a genuine scripted language — perhaps more than one. Decoding them occupied the rest of his life.

The excavation of Knossos began in 1900. Shortly afterward, they uncovered a veritable labyrinth of rooms which Evans concluded was a palace. There was even a "throne room," which from the shape of the seat of the throne, Evans concluded, must have belonged to a woman. "It figures," Anne says. There were friezes on the wall with the images of bulls. Evans immediately thought of the myth of the Minotaur — the bull-headed monster which had been kept in a labyrinth at Knossos by King Minotor. The civilization that produced these artifacts he called Minoan. Evans and his diggers began turning up tablets with writings similar to those seen on the seal stones. These tablets, which were sort of rectangular in shape, were made of clay and could fit nicely into one hand. The scribes must have written on them with a stylus. The ones that were found looked burnt and had the consistency of ceramic. To Evans, this meant that at some point the palace had gone up in flames.

Evans had a theory of written language. First came the drawings — the pictographs from which the hieroglyphics were abstracted. A further abstraction occurred when the hieroglyphs became simple geometric figures. The distinction among these classes was fuzzy. A sign became abstract when Evans could no longer identify a face. He called the scripts with these simple figures "linear." His tablets seemed to divide into two classes, which he called "Linear A" and "Linear B." He that "Linear A" was the earliest form and may have been the basis for "Linear B." He made several correct conclusions about the writing on these tablets. He mentioned that it went from left to right and that there were numbers in the decimal system. He found symbols that appeared to function as word-dividers. Where he went terribly wrong was to assume that every pictorial symbol was a representation of the object depicted. Something that looked like a double axe, for example, was, he taught, simply a drawing of a double axe. For some time, the same mistake was made in the decipherment of the Egyptian hieroglyphics until it was understood that it was a syllabic language. He insisted that Linear A and B were the written version of a language that he called "Minoan." Nothing would change his mind about this and anyone who disagreed would not be allowed to work at Knossos.

Hieroglyphics

Linear A

Linear B

I have reached the place in my discourse where it is time to introduce Michael Ventris, but I think we need a break. A trip to the nearby gelateria is called for. In addition to the gelati, I like to watch the courtship rituals of the young. When I first went there with Anne, I told her that I had tried to write the worst romantic poem ever written. It began

'Twas on a lovely day like this.
When first we watched the watercress
Clasp snowy dewdrops
To its breast.

Anne said she thought it was a strong candidate.

I always order the same gelato — the stracciatella. It has a more romantic ring than "rocky road." I love those Italian words that seem to arise like bubbles. Take the word for a trim in a barber shop *una spuntatina*. You can't make it up.

There is a couple we focus on. He looks like an ur-geek, the kind in my day one would have avoided at all costs. The chances of his finding a date with a Radcliffe girl would have been nil. But since Bill Gates and Mark Zuckerberg made geekdom bankable, there is hope for everybody. She has

long black braids, which she is constantly twisting. I ask Anne what the braided one is thinking. "She is wondering," Anne says, "if anything she has been saying makes the slightest sense." I know what he is thinking. "Let us get back to my place as soon as possible." I tell this to Anne and say what would worry me would be the next morning — when would she leave? "You should see Doctor Lipmann — or whatever his name is — as soon as possible," she says. It is time for Ventris.

Michael Ventris and William Jones were both in their own ways linguistic geniuses; Jones was broader. Ventris was believed to have known about a dozen languages. Jones knew forty one. He translated from the Persian, and in the circle of Samuel Johnson he was known as "Persian Jones." He thought his best language was Sanskrit, which he studied intensively with a pandit. Among other things, he translated the Sanskrit epic, Kalidasa's *Abhiknana Shakuntala*, which gave English-speaking readers their first view of the richness of the Indian literature. For both men, linguistics was an avocation. Jones was a lawyer and jurist, while Ventris was an architect. Both men died young — Jones at forty seven and Ventris at thirty four. Both men had a connection with India. Jones was a judge there and Ventris' father was a lieutenant colonel in the British army. During one of his holidays in Britain, he married Anna Dorthea Janasz, a Polish beauty with a good deal of money. Their only child, Michael, was born in Hertfordshire in 1922.

As a boy, Ventris was sickly so his parents decided for some reason that he would be better off living in Switzerland. He did his first schooling in Gstaad, where the classes were taught in French and German. He learned the local Swiss-German dialect as well as the Polish of his mother. This lasted until 1931 when the family returned to England and his parents got divorced. Ventris joined the Stowe school, where he learned Latin and Greek. The event that changed his life was a lecture in London by Evans. He was eighty five and used a walking stick. He exhibited some Linear B tablets and mentioned that they were an un-deciphered Minoan language. Ventris decided that he would be the one to decipher them.

His father died in 1938, and after the German invasion of Poland in 1939, his mother lost her money. They were left destitute. Ventris was awarded a scholarship to study at Stowe school. His mother fell deeper and deeper into depression, and Ventris took refuge with the family of a Russian sculptor named Naum Gabo. Gabo, who was Jewish, had migrated to various countries before finally landing In England. He had studied Einstein's relativity theory and tried to introduce the ideas into his sculptures. He finally emigrated to the United States and died in Connecticut in 1977. Gabo understood that Ventris was something special. He taught him Russian and became Ventris's real father figure. After Stowe Ventris decided that he would become an architect. He enrolled in an architectural school, where he met and married his wife who came from a well-to-do family. He never had a chance to finish his courses because in 1942 he was drafted. He chose the Royal Air Force and was trained as a navigator — something that he thought was more interesting than being a pilot. He took part in the bombing campaign over Germany, where there was every possibility of him being shot down and killed. One wonders with Ventris whether there was always some dark demon lurking. After the war, he was stationed in Germany, where because of his fluency in Russian he was involved in some kind of intelligence work. A mystery is whether any of this involved deciphering codes, which would have been valuable as training for deciphering Linear B. Upon returning to England, he completed his studies and began an architectural career. He was certainly a competent, if not an outstanding, architect, but his real intellectual energies were focused on Linear B.

Ventris decided that the underlying language was Etruscan. This replaced a mystery by an enigma. In decoding these languages, there are three interesting cases: the language is known but the script is unknown, the language is unknown by the script is known, and finally they are both unknown. This is obviously the most difficult, if not impossible, case. By insisting that the Linear B tablets were written in "Minoan," he chose this case. Ventris went for Etruscan. The Etruscan people, whoever they were, migrated in about 800 BC to what is now Tuscany. They must have been a fairly jolly folk since the relics are decorated with wine and women. They left some of their written language to be deciphered. It turned out to be written using the Greek alphabet, which was learned from the Phoenicians who invented it. Thus, all the words were known since they could be spelled out. What was and is completely unknown is what language they are in. It is certainly not Greek. Ventris thought it might be some kind of proto-Etruscan. In 1950, Ventris sent a questionnaire to twelve scholars working in the field. He wanted to know where things stood. Ten of them answered and one of them — Alice Kober from Brooklyn College — answered only that she did not have time. This was true quite literally. She was dying of breast cancer which would take her life that year. But before she died, she made the first real advancements deciphering the language, from which everything else followed.

By the time the dust settled, there were eighty-nine different signs. They had been given numbers by Kober and the American archeologist Emmett Bennett. They had additional signs to work with because tablets had been discovered at Pylos on the Greek mainland by another American archeologist named Carl Blegen. This material was not in control of Evans who rationed out his tablets. This numerical system saved drawing a picture of a sign or a group of signs every time one wanted to discuss them. The number of signs was too few for an ideogrammatic language like Chinese and too many for an alphabetical script. It must be a syllabic script like the hieroglyphics. But she argued that the language was almost certainly inflected. Hence, you would expect to find groups of words that had the same symbols except a few that would indicate the inflection. She identified several groups of three which came to be called later, somewhat irreverently, as "Kober's triplets." Here are several examples.

Abb.: Zusammenstellung identischer Zeichengruppen mit alternierenden Endzeichen bei Arthur Evans (A) und Alice Kober (B)
A: nach A. Evans, The Palace of Minos at Knossos IV (1935) 714 Abb. 695
B nach A. E. Kober, The Minoan Scripts: Fact and Theory, AJA 52, 1948, 97 Abb. 8

Kober decided that Linear B must be an articulated language similar to, for example, Latin. Hence, the different endings must represent different cases like the Latin *domini, dominum,* and *dominus.* They probably had consonants in common but had different vowels and she made guesses as to what these might be. When Ventris read this work, he became obsessed. He quit his job at the Ministry of Education and devoted himself full-time to Linear B. His family already felt that he was remote and now he became single-minded. His daughter recalls that she never really had a father or a real home. When she went away to school, they would rent her room and she would come back to find her things gone. He was on a drug — Linear B.

"I see a crash landing somewhere," Anne said. "I think you are right." I said. "There is a parallel here which I will get back to. While Ventris was doing his thing Edmund Hillary was indulging his obsession — to become the first man to climb Everest."

What Ventris did was to construct grids. This was formalizing what Kober had begun. His technique makes me wonder if he had had formal training in code breaking or it was something he just made up. He made grids. This one is a very simplified version. Remember that each sign stands for a syllable with vowels and consonants. If you read across the row, they all have the same consonant but the different columns have different vowels.

This grid has them put in but remember that Ventris did not know what they were.

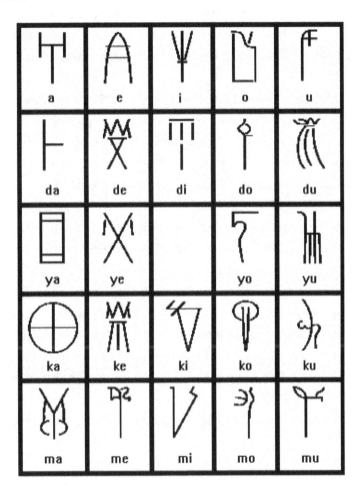

His breakthrough came when he realized that one symbol was probably "a" and another was probably "mi." He then had a stroke of genius. He guessed that some town in Crete was being spelled out, and the one he could find in Homer was Amiso. This gave him "so" from which he could get "Knossos," which in turn gave him more letters. These gave him no clue as to the underlying language. Lots of American towns like "Oswego" have Indian names. Then he came up with something that looked like the Greek word for "coriander" but this could have been a loan word from the Minoan. Now, he looked at the declensions for "boy" and "girl." Things began appearing more and more Greek. "The Greek chimera again raises its head," he wrote in one of the work notes he freely circulated.

Evans had died in 1941, but it wasn't until 1952 that photographs of some of the tablets he had found at Knossos were published. The BBC Third Programme decided to make a broadcast about this. God knows what kind of audience they expected. But they asked Ventris to be the narrator. This was a very odd choice. Ventris had no academic standing. He was known only to a few fellow devotees of the decipherment to whom he was circulating his work notes. One of them must have recommended him. But a professor of classics at Cambridge heard the program and thought that a colleague of his — a linguist named John Chadwick, who had just come to Cambridge — might be interested. He knew that Chadwick was trying his hand at the decipherment. Chadwick was very interested because he had come to the conclusion that the underlying language was an ancient pre-Homeric form of Greek. He contacted Ventris. Ventris's reaction was not what I might have expected. I thought he might have brushed Chadwick off as a parvenu. Not at all. He embraced him and proposed a collaboration. In short order, they were deciphering entire sentences. Chadwick knew a number of words in Ancient Greek which he contributed.

In some sense, the results were a disappointment. They were mainly accounts with the numbers of various quantities. There were few flashes such as "At Pylos, slaves of the priestess on account of sacred gold:14women…" Whatever this means it says something odd about that society. By the fall of 1952, Chadwick and Ventris were writing their great paper "Evidence for Greek Dialect in the Mycenaean Archives." They still had some lingering doubts when they received a letter from Carl Blegen, who had discovered the first Linear B tablets at Pylos in 1939. During the war, they had been hidden in the Bank of Athens. Now, he was back in Pylos and had found a tablet that he felt Ventris must see.

At first sight, the tablet which I showed to Anne seems entirely banal.

Ta 641

It has the prosaic labeling Ta 641. The key thing to observe are the two vases that stand on three legs. These two are denoted by the adjective *tripode*. That the three-legged objects would be described as "tripods" is not so surprising. What is surprising until you understand it is the form the word takes. This has to do with the fact that in early Greek two of anything had a special form. The word *tripode* is telling us that there are two three-legged urns. No more proof of the underlying language was needed. By the way, the original is in the Mycenaean Room of the National Archeological Museum in Athens. It is obscured by the displays of Schliemann's gold artifacts. I was so excited when I saw it that I wanted to tell everyone in the museum. A guard came over and told me that I was making too much noise.

Mount Everest was conquered on the May 29, 1953 by Hillary and Tenzing. The Chadwick-Ventris paper was published in June and on June 24, Ventris gave a lecture in London. The *London Times* called the discovery the "Everest of Greek archeology." In 1955, Ventris was awarded the "order of this British empire." Hillary had been named a Knight Commander of the British Empire in 1953. He did some further Himalayan climbing for the fun of it and founded things like a school and a hospital for the Sherpas. Tenzing founded an academy in Darjeeling to teach Sherpas technical climbing. I met them both in Kathmandu. They seemed like very happy people. I think that Ventris was at loose ends. He had fulfilled his life's ambition. Was he now going to spend the rest of it designing schools? His marriage was coming apart. His wife mentioned that for years they had had nothing to talk about. He was estranged from his children. What exactly happened late at night on

September 6, 1956 is something we will never know. We do know that he collided with a lorry while driving and was killed instantly. His mother had committed suicide on June 16, 1940. You can draw your own conclusions.

I told Anne, "I have talked enough and now I want you to explain women to me." "We can't be explained," Anne said. "Freud who was much smarter than you are said that he could never understand what we wanted…. I suggest that you get over it and get yourself a pet."

# Chapter 5

"There was a young man who said: 'Run!'
The end of the world has begun!
The one I fear most
Is that damn' Holy Ghost,
I can handle the Father and Son."

                 — In a letter from von Neumann to his wife.

Oh, the Rand Corporation's the boon of the world,
They think all day long for a fee.
They sit and play games about going up in flames;

For counters they use you and me, honey bee,
For counters they use you and me.

Malvina Reynolds

"Sherlock Holmes, pursued by his opponent, Moriarity, leaves for Dover. The train stops at a station on the way, and he alights there rather than traveling on to Dover. He has seen Moriarity at the railway station, recognizes that he is very clever, and expects that Moriarity will take a special faster train in order to catch him in Dover. Holmes' anticipation turns out to be correct. But what if Moriarity had been still more clever, had estimated Holmes' mental abilities better and had foreseen his actions accordingly? Then obviously he would have traveled to the intermediate station. Holmes, again, would have had to calculate that, and he himself would have decided to go on to Dover. Whereupon Moriarity would have 'reacted' differently. Because of so much thinking they might not have been able to act at all or the intellectually weaker of the two would have surrendered to the other in the Victoria Station, since the whole flight would have become unnecessary. Examples of this kind can be drawn from everywhere. However, chess, strategy, etc., presuppose expert knowledge which encumbers the example unnecessarily."

Oskar Morgenstern 1935

"What are we to make of a civilization which has always regarded ethics as an essential part of human life and … which has not been able to talk about the prospects of killing almost everybody, except in prudential and game-theoretic terms?"

J. Robert Oppenheimer

Elena and Stanley have not been in the park for a while. Anne tells me that she has gone to California where she consults for the RAND Corporation. "Unlike you," Anne adds, "she has her PhD in mathematics. You missed the boat with that one." "I never get involved with a woman who has a higher degree than I do and that includes dermatologists," I reply.

"She told me that her specialty was the theory of games. What is that? The only game for which I had a theory was 'spin the bottle.' I found that if I jiggled the table I could get the bottle to stop in front of the boy I actually wanted to kiss. Where are they now? *Mais où sont les neiges d'antan?*" "You know before I learned French in Paris I always thought that this was '*Mais où sont les neiges d'Antoine?*' and wondered if Antoine was a ski instructor" "It might have been '*Mais où sont les nages d'Antoine*' if he was a life guard," Anne added, "or '*Mais où sont les nuages d'Antoine*' if he was a weatherman." "Let's play tic tac toe," I said. "Why?" Anne asks sensibly. "I can show you a little about game theory," I answered. "I forgot how to play it," she acknowledged, "At some point I decided that it was a stupid game so I just forgot how to play it." "It is a stupid game but it is stupid in an intelligent way." "That is sometimes how I feel about you," Anne noted but I refused to be distracted. "We will draw nine squares like this

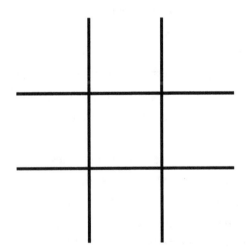

"Now you can go first and if you like take 'O' as your sign. I will take 'X'. The idea is for us to make our marks successively in the squares. The first person to get three X's or three O's in a row wins. If neither of us can do this the game ends as a tie. Go ahead." Anne puts her O in the center. I put my X in a corner. We take several moves and we tie. Next, Anne puts her

O in a corner and we make several moves and we tie; next, Anne puts an O in an edge and after several moves we tie. "You cheated," Anne says. "No I didn't. There is a guaranteed strategy given your moves that will produce at least a tie. There are 26,830 possible distinct games and if I play the correct strategy I can never lose. If I start first and I play the correct strategy I will either win or tie depending on what you do. If we both play the correct strategy all our games will end up in a tie which is why it is a stupid game. Little kids who play it usually don't get it and they can go on for hours. There are computer sites which let you play one game after the other. If a little kid gets it right away watch out we may be dealing with another von Neumann." "God," she says, "It's von Neumann again. He keeps popping up like a toy balloon." "He was one of the things that persuaded me to quit mathematics. When I was at Harvard I heard him give a lecture on the computer and the brain — I will tell you about it later. It was like champagne for the mind. I had never heard a lecture like that before, or since. I went to the library and got out a couple of his books. I decided that there was no point. I had better do something else.

"In the 1920's he got interested in the theory of games. I know that he liked to play poker and that he was not especially good at it. He seems to have found it difficult to conceal his pleasure at being dealt a good hand. There was a very distinguished French mathematician named Emile Borel who wrote several papers on the strategy of games in the 1920s. This may be what set von Neumann off. He said later that game theory really did not begin until his 1928 paper, which must have made Borel feel good. By this time, Borel was in the French National Assembly and had become Minister of the Marine. He was doing mathematics only part time. Tic tac toe is a very simple illustration of von Neumann's main result. What is characteristic of tic-tac-toe?" "It is boring." "Besides that, it is a two-person game with a finite number of moves — nine in this instance. It is also what is called a zero sum game. If I win, you lose although we can tie. I have said that there is a strategy which if I start first and use it I cannot lose. There is also a strategy which if you start second and use it you cannot lose. The existence of such a strategy for this kind of game is known as a 'mini-max theorem'. What von Neumann showed was that for any game with these specifications there must be such a strategy. His theorem does not tell you how to find it. Checkers is an interesting case. There are 500 billion billion possible checker games. But according to von Neumann's theorem there must be a mini-max strategy. It took a very powerful computer program to find it. Chess is even worse and it is unlikely that any one will find it." "Good," says Anne.

"Von Neumann thought about the economic implications of game theory and in 1932 he attended a conference in Vienna where he lectured on what some of them might be. Gödel's friend Oskar Morgenstern was an economics professor at the university and he must have heard the lecture. Von Neumann wrote it up in German in 1937. It concerned the mathematics of an expanding economy. One wonders if he and Morgenstern discussed these ideas back then. Morgenstern came here in 1938 and stayed in Princeton once the Germans took over Austria. I have often wondered how their collaboration began. Did they meet at tea at the Institute or at one of the parties that von Neumann liked to give? What did they say to each other that began it? We know how it ended. In 1944 they published a masterpiece *The Theory of Games and Economic Behavior.* It is interesting that von Neumann put his name first instead of in alphabetical order. I guess that means that he did the mathematical heavy lifting. But Morgenstern was no slouch.

"What is remarkable to me in that von Neumann did this work during the war. The preface to the first edition is dated January 1943. I am not aware that Morgenstern did any war work but von Neumann was up to his neck in it. In the summer of 1944 he began consulting at the Aberdeen Proving Ground in Maryland. The people there were building the first electronic programmable computer. They were going to use it for calculating the trajectories of shells fired from cannons. Von Neumann heard about it that summer from someone who was working on the project and became very interested. What he did was somewhat similar to what he did for the quantum theory. The development of that theory did not need von Neumann. The physicists were doing fine. But once he got interested he set up the whole formal mathematical basis for it. I think the same thing is true of the computer. The engineers at Aberdeen were doing fine. I think that they would have come up with essentially the same computer with or without von Neumann. What von Neumann did was to make it systematic. He wrote a classic report and thereafter computers were said to employ the 'von Neumann architecture' which made the engineers feel good, as you might imagine. Later there were lawsuits. But von Neumann's interest in the computer did not have to do with artillery shells. He was working on the atomic bomb."

Anne was clearly not happy about the bomb. I told her that it was going to get worse. Once the bomb had been built, von Neumann thought that it would be a good idea to drop a few on the Russians before they had a chance to do the same to us. "That's sick," Anne said. "I agree and I guess Einstein who was his colleague must have felt the same. He referred to him as a *denke Tier* — a think animal" — not a very flattering description. But during the war we thought we were in a race with the Germans so everyone including von Neumann was going all out. "When I was at Harvard I met a young physics professor. When he was eighteen and had not yet graduated from Harvard he was recruited to go to Los Alamos. He went with his roommate who was also a physics student. The train stopped in Lamy, New Mexico — not far from Santa Fe. They then went to 101 East Palace where there was an office to welcome them. After their credentials were vetted they were shuttled up to the mesa on which Los Alamos sat.

"There was another passenger who introduced himself as 'Mister Newman'. My friend knew it was von Neumann but simply went along with it as did his roommate. This was some security ruse. The only problem was that his college roommate turned out to be a Soviet spy.

"Von Neumann must have been one of the best consultants who ever lived. He had PhDs in both chemical engineering and mathematics. He had an incredible memory and could do very complex arithmetical computations in his head very fast. He invented the basic design of the bomb that flattened Nagasaki. The calculations needed to build it were so complex that even he could not do them in his head. That is why he was so eager to build a computer. One of the first things the first real computer was assigned to do was to calculate things that were needed to build the hydrogen bomb. Your laptop has a tainted history."

"I feel the need of an afternoon snack," Anne said, so we headed back to the gelati place. A very odd-looking fellow carrying a heavy brief case walked in. "I am sure that he is the world's greatest expert on something," I said. "Maybe phonemes." "What are phonemes?" Anne asked. "They are the sounds that make the difference between 'Anne' and 'ant'," I explained. "Is this something that I absolutely need to know?" she asked. "Yes," I replied as we finished our gelati. As we walked past the fellow, he was saying "madder" and "mother" into a tape recorder.

When we got back, I told Anne something about the RAND Corporation. "RAND," I explained "stands for 'research and development'." "Shouldn't there be another D?" she asked. "No," in Southern California where the company was founded "and" is pronounced "an." It is a matter of conserving phonemes. Anyway in 1945, using leftover defense funds, the Army Air Force gave the Douglas Aircraft Company ten million dollars to found a think tank that would be dedicated to solving problems for the Air Force. They eventually set it up as an independent entity in Santa Monica a couple of blocks from the beach. By this time, it resembled more a small university than any kind of industrial research center. But it was largely devoted to nuclear weapons strategy. I didn't know this when I went out there for an interview about the time I was getting my master's degree. The building was very southern California. It's sort of pinkish. I stayed in a motel near the beach and had several papaya smoothies. It was a perfect place to think about nuclear weapons. I flunked my interview. The guy asked me what I was working on and I said "nothing: I was just taking courses. That was the wrong answer so he more of less said don't call us, we'll call you. But I did get to meet Herman Kahn."

"Who's that?" Anne asked. "When I met him he was blimpish and had the complexion of a poached carp. It was hard to believe that during the war when he was in the army he had been a telephone linesman in Burma. I just couldn't see him getting up on a ladder. He had been a physics major at UCLA and went back to finish his undergraduate degree. He then went on to Caltech for his PhD but had to drop out because of money. He decided to go into real estate. I bet he was very good at it. I could see him selling igloos to Eskimos. 'It comes with a heated swimming pool.' Now the really odd part is that he went from this to working on the hydrogen bomb with people like von Neumann and Edward Teller. They must have thought that he was pretty smart because they got him a job at RAND. I would be surprised if Herman had the technical competence to contribute anything to that side of what RAND was doing — the game theory for example. But what he lacked in competence he made up in chutzpa. He invented a shtick for himself that was pure genius. He was going to 'think about the unthinkable.'"

"How do you do that?" Anne asked. "Precisely," I answered. "It would be like driving a car with all the gears stripped. I think it led to brain freeze. They had to have Herman recite

Simple Simon met a pieman going to the fair;
Said Simple Simon to the pieman 'Let me taste your ware',

Over and over until his brain became unlocked. It was something to see. You could sell tickets. What he did think about was almost as absurd."

"What was that?"

"He thought we could actually *win* a nuclear war. There would of course be collateral damage. A few of our cities like New York and Washington would be gone. There would be megadeaths. But in short order people would be going back on the beach in Santa Monica, ordering shrimp tostados and double double cheeseburgers. Some of the Russian cities like Moscow and Leningrad would be gone, but the Russians would be crying 'uncle.' To whom it is not clear since the authorities in Washington would have been vaporized. The Air Force brass that was bankrolling RAND loved it. They might have a chance of trying out their new toys. Herman was like a pig in parsley. He became a celebrity. His book *Thinking about the Unthinkable* became a best seller. He gave me an autographed copy. It's on the shelf there next to my guidebook to Australia where I thought of going. The best touch I thought came in the matter of irradiated crops. These would produce cancer so they should be fed to the elderly who would surely croak of something else. But poor Herman. He never met a corn beef sandwich or a cheesecake he didn't fall in love with. The poor bastard died of a stroke at 61. What a loss!

"Von Neumann was very happy to consult for RAND. He liked Los Angeles and the mathematicians at RAND were very good especially in the summer when the consultants gathered. Von Neumann was the master virtuoso performing for the lesser virtuosi. One of these was John Nash. He had chosen to do his graduate work at Princeton, where game theory was an active subject. He had written a twenty seven-page thesis in 1950 in which he made an essential advance. In 1994, he shared the Nobel Prize in Economics for this work but in between his life had been one of desperation. I will tell you about that when I have explained what he did. Here is a little example.

"You and I are competitive automobile dealers of the French 'Poubelles.'"

"Don't you mean 'Peugots?'"

"No, I am trying to make my example as realistic as possible. The owners refer to them affectionately as 'Pous.' In any event we have received our fall allotment and we want to set prices but we are not allowed to collude. To make the example precise we have three possibilities, 'high', 'medium' and 'low,' If we could collude we would set our prices 'high' and screw the consumer which is what happens in the real world. Here is how you would reason."

"How do you know how I would reason?"

"Fair enough but indulge me hypothetically, you would say if I set my price high and you set yours to medium people will find out and I will go out of business. If I set my price to medium you will set yours to low and again I will be clobbered. The only rational thing for me to do is to set my price low. You will come to the same conclusion and we will both set our prices low. This is an example of what is known as a Nash equilibrium. Once it is attained the situation is stable. Von Neumann and Morgenstern argued that such a strategy must exist for finite, zero-sum games but Nash showed that it must also exist for non-zero-sum games which is the situation for most real-world situations. It took some time for Nash's result to sink in and by the time it did he was in deep trouble.

"Nash began consulting at RAND in the summer of 1950. But it was in the summer of 1952 while at RAND that he probably had his first homosexual experience. The next year a somewhat older woman with whom Nash was having an affair had his son. In the summer of 1954 when he was again at RAND he was arrested in a police sting looking for homosexuals and he was dismissed from RAND. In 1957 he married a woman who was one of the rare coeds at MIT where Nash had been teaching. What she knew about his homosexual affairs is not clear. They apparently continued. By 1959 it was clear that Nash was seriously mentally ill. Indeed, for the next thirty years he was in and out of institutions. But during this time his mathematical colleagues did not desert him. My Harvard tutor George Mackey was a frequent visitor at McLean hospital. Mackey had an almost childlike curiosity about things. He was genuinely puzzled by what form the messages from extraterrestrials came to Nash. Nash told him that they took the same form that his mathematical ideas did and so he took them seriously. The remarkable thing about Nash's mental illness was that it went into remission. He and his wife had divorced in 1962 after her having given birth to a son. But she agreed to let him live with her and their son in Princeton starting in 1970. By this time no one knew him and Nash took to leaving not unfriendly notes on people's desks and blackboards. He did some simple problems on one of the university computers and began attending seminars.

"Nineteen ninety four was the fiftieth anniversary of the publication of the von Neumann–Morgenstern book and it was decided that a Nobel Prize might be appropriate for game theory. You have to understand that the Nobel Prize in economics is different. The money comes from the Central Bank of Sweden and not the Nobel will. But it is administered by the Royal Swedish Academy. Nash was a clear candidate but the worry was his mental condition. So they sent a spy to scout out the situation. He met with Nash and some of the other Princeton mathematicians and decided that Nash was no crazier than they were. So he got his prize. It's strange. The day after it was announced a friend of mine who teaches about cosmology at Princeton had been on TV and ran into Nash whom he did not know. Nash said to him, 'You're famous. I saw you on TV.' There was a movie about him in which Russel Crowe plays Nash. I suspect that he has less understanding of the mathematics than Molly.

"Speaking of Molly, let's take her out for a walk. I need a scene change and some fresh air. I am sure Molly won't mind." We head for the park, Molly in tow. Stanley is not there but she has some new friends. When she brings one of them over, I give them both a treat. I want Molly's friends to think of me as a nice person. When we get back, I tell Anne about RAND and game theory — RAND people took to it like bears to honey.

"It began as fun and games. It later developed into plans for nuclear strategy. Whenever I think of that I am always reminded of what David Hilbert, von Neumann's mathematical hero, said about astrology. He said that if the ten smartest people in the world got together they could not think up anything as stupid as astrology."

"That's hurtful," Anne said. "I hadn't realized," I replied.

"Some time ago I told you about a dream I had. In the dream Doctor Levman has taken you and me prisoner. We are kept in separate cells and cannot communicate, but Doctor Levman can make visits to us. On his first visit to me he says that I have two choices, to confess or deny. To what, he does not explain. He then tells me the possibilities. If I confess and you deny I will serve two and a third years and you will go free. If I deny and you confess then I will go free and you will serve for two and a third years. If I confess and you confess we will serve for only a day as a reward for our honesty. If we both deny we will both serve 10 days. He tells me that he has made the same offer to you. He gives me nineteen minutes to make up my mind.

"Here is how I reason. Suppose you confess. I have two choices, to confess or deny. If I confess I will serve for a day but if I deny I will go free.

So it is worth my while to deny. If you deny and I confess you will go free and I will serve the two and a third years. If I deny we will serve for only ten days. Hence no matter what you do it is better for me to deny. But you will come to the same conclusion and hence we will both deny and serve for ten days. But this is not the best outcome. The best outcome is for both of us to confess. This is the Nash equilibrium strategy since it makes both of us happiest but our misguided logic would lead us to reject it. When the game is stated this way, it is called 'the prisoner's dilemma'. It was invented at RAND but in a form involving money. The principle inventor was a man called Merrill Flood. I suppose he might have been considered for the Nobel, but he died in 1991. He collaborated with another RAND mathematician named Melvin Dresher, but he died in 1992 so Nash was left standing. Flood thought the game was interesting but had no idea of the sensation it would make. This happened because a distinguished Princeton mathematician named Albert Tucker who had actually been one of Nash's teachers and was a consultant at RAND had agreed to give a lecture on game theory in the psychology department at Stanford. He thought that he could get it over better if he converted the money game to a game about prisoners. He gave it its name 'the prisoner's dilemma'. The forests of trees that have been cut down for the papers which have been written about this game maketh one to weep. Also the game was taken by some people as a guide to how real prisoners might behave. Can you imagine any circumstances where this might happen? I want my lawyer.

"I told you I visited RAND for a job interview. I did not get to see much of the inner workings but the exterior was remarkable. It was like a small posh university. There was a nice restaurant where you could buy papaya salads and then eat them outside with zephyrs from the Pacific wafting over you. There was a tennis court. Long legged California girls walked around. And there was Herman upstairs behind armed guards thinking about mega deaths. It buggers the imagination."

"Do you mean it beggars the imagination?" Anne asked.

"Possibly," I answered.

"Of course there were the game theorists with the nuclear strategies which now included Inter Continental Ballistic Missiles to intercontinental ballistic missiles which RAND had a big hand in developing. They were looking for Nash equilibria. I can't help thinking about an experience I had. When I was at Harvard I dated a Radcliffe girl who was as cute as a button. We were sort of buddies and went to coffee shops and the movies from time to time. I knew she lived somewhere near Boston but not exactly where. One day she asked if I would like to come to Sunday lunch and meet her parents. She told me that the Sunday lunches were always special and there were guests from the university and elsewhere. I said that I would be delighted and she gave me a map. I had a dreadful old Morris Minor convertible at the time but I thought with care it could be coaxed into making the trip. I followed the map and turned off on a country road which went through a kind of forest. Finally, I came to some houses including one very large one at the center. It began to dawn on me that this forest and the houses all belonged to her family. Their name rang a sort of bell and I realized that these were people who must have come over on the Mayflower or a sister ship. I was greeted warmly by her mother who was perfectly delightful. Years later long after her daughter and I had gone our separate ways her mother paid me a visit while she was passing through Paris. *La Dolce Vita* was playing. I had seen it but I thought she might like it which she did — enormously.

"She told me what had happened to part of her woods. The Army had taken it over and surrounded it by a fence. She had no idea why. But she continued to walk near the fence with her dogs. Sometimes the soldiers would come out and talk to her. They would show her pictures of their families or their girlfriends and she would bring along a cake or a pie which she gave them. A few years later, it was revealed that this was an antiaircraft missile battery. I couldn't help thinking what if it had been an ICBM launching site with nuclear warheads ready to go, part of some game theory strategy. What would happen, I wondered, if the soldiers were out talking to this grandmotherly lady when there was an alert. Would the whole game theory strategy evaporate or would this have been included as a possibility in the game?

"By the early 1960s the great days of the RAND gamesmen were over. Nash was gone. Flood had left for Columbia. Von Neumann had died in 1957. Herman had left to be one of the founders of the Hudson Institute and had turned his attention to Vietnam. But the days at RAND sure were fun while they lasted."

# Chapter 6

"A chain of eight volcanoes known as the Virunga Volcanoes runs through a western section of the Rift Valley, forming part of the border between Uganda, Democratic Republic of Congo (formerly Zaire) and Rwanda. These spectacular mountains and the nearby Bwindi Impenetrable National Park in Uganda are the last refuges of the most endangered of the gorilla subspecies, the mountain gorilla. Only about 630 of these individuals remain."

Wikipedia

"I will jump into the river to save. 2 brothers or 8 cousins."

J.B.S. Haldane

"It is an occupational risk of biologists to claim, towards the end of their careers, that the problems which they have not solved are insoluble."

John Maynard Smith

A man goes for a walk in the country and runs into a shepherd. The shepherd says if you guess the number of sheep I have I will give you one. The man guesses 83. "That's right," says the shepherd, "and now I will guess your profession. You are a mathematical biologist." "Yes, how did you guess?" "You picked up a dog."

I told Anne that during my two-year world wandering I decided to visit the mountain gorillas. This is not like visiting the zoo. A very limited number of visitors are allowed to approach them so you have to reserve your place long in advance and make a pretty substantial down payment. The few gorillas that are left live in three countries: the Congo, Rwanda, and Uganda. They of course do not know this. They roam around what is left of their habitat crossing freely from one country to another. But we have to choose so I chose the Congo. This meant flying to Kigali, the capital of Rwanda, from Brussels, taking a minivan to Goma in eastern Congo and joining the rest of the gorilla group. We had been warned that there would be a jungle trek so the group was suitably outfitted with pith helmets and the like. We had nothing in common except that we wanted to see the gorillas and were affluent enough to afford an expensive trip. There were few enough of us so that we could fit into two Land Rovers.

We left Goma before daybreak since we had to be at the entrance to the reserve at our appointed time. We were told that if we arrived late our spot would be given away to people camped in the area hoping to get a chance at a viewing and that we would have to get back in line, probably for months. It was a spectacular drive that passed by the Nyiragongo volcano that was still active. Then we left the main road and headed uphill toward the base of one of the Virunga volcanoes which was not active and on whose sides the mountain gorillas lived. There was thick mud on the road and one of the Land Rovers got stuck. We got it out with the help of some people from a nearby village. They looked pretty poor and we gave them some money for their help. I could not help thinking of what they must think of us.

The Land Rovers got us to the base of a grassy hill. There were tents all over the place with people who were waiting either for their turn or to pick up any unused reservation. At the top of the hill was the entrance station. We handed over our reservation slip and paid the rest of the money we owed. We each got a set of instructions which made it clear that there wasn't a money-back guarantee that we would see any gorillas. We were then introduced to our two guides one of whom was carrying a rifle. There were poachers. We started along a road on which I am sure a jeep could have driven. Then it was a path. The guide leading us then stopped and headed into the jungle cutting something of a track with a machete. The vegetation got thicker and the going got harder and harder. A cynical thought came into my mind. Maybe this is a scam. Maybe after running us through all of this thick, almost impenetrable vegetation, the guide seeing that we had had enough would say that he was sorry but the gorillas have gone off today. We would be so grateful for calling a halt to our trek that there would be no objections.

The guide leading us then stopped and put his hand to his lips. I thought, "Here it comes." He then pointed upwards and just above me was the most extraordinary being that I have ever seen. It was a male silverback gorilla. It was huge. It could have been over five feet tall and weighed more than four hundred pounds. It was in its nest, peacefully eating some leaves. It looked down at me with an expression of incredible sadness. I wondered whether it was sad about its own fate or mine. I felt completely safe. This being which could have destroyed me with one arm had no special curiosity and certainly no bad intentions. We walked into a clearing and there was a small troop of gorillas. I think they were the females that belonged to the silverback. One of them had a baby and she held it up so we could see it. I know this sounds incredible but that is what happened. We all saw it. We did not want to leave but we could hear another group coming behind us. On the way back to Goma no one said anything. It was as if this had happened in a dream.

"You make them sound almost human," Anne said.

"Yes and no. We share a number of genes but they are not our ancestors. We are two branches of a common ancestor. Here is what gives me pause for thought. It is said that *Homo* sapiens, our branch, has existed for maybe 150,000 years. How many years to a generation? Now it may be twenty five but earlier it was probably closer to fifteen. So there have been, say 10,000 generations since the beginning. So let us count backwards. I have two parents and each of them had two parents and so on. If we ask how many ancestors do I have going back to the beginning it is more than the suggested number of atoms in the visible universe. The only way out is if we are all descended from a small tribe. That means you and I are probably related. I hate to admit that, since if our relationship were not Platonic it would be incestuous."

"Yippee!" said Anne.

"You know I never liked biology. It is too hard. In physics you start with a few quarks and predict every particle that exists, or most of them. In mathematics we start with some axioms and derive all the decidable theorems. But in biology no one could have predicted a mountain gorilla, or a giraffe or a hippopotamus for that matter — or us. We and they are all evolutionary accidents. Also I can't stand the names in biology. 'Allele' — the name gives me a headache and it is defined by terms like heterozygotes. Maybe if I knew Greek I would feel better about it. Αλληλόμορφα γονίδια.

"But I can say this. Outside of zoos I think that mountain gorillas are doomed. They don't start breeding until they are past ten and then infants are produced every three or four years. Under the best circumstances it would be hard to maintain the population. But with so few, the gene pool is limited and this degrades the species. They are now contracting human diseases from the contact but without the tourists the temptation of the locals would be to convert more and more of their habitat into farm land. There is poaching. A gorilla is a valuable item. You can eat the meat and mount the head and paws on your mantle. Look at poor Diane Fossey. She worked with the gorillas in Rwanda just over the top of the mountains we were on. She made friends with them and had poachers arrested. But her favorite gorilla whom she called 'digit' was killed and his hands sold as ash trays. She was murdered in 1965. I wish that I had better news but I don't."

"What a terrible story," Anne says

"For some absurd reason it reminds me of the Yiddish proverb 'Worries go down better with soup'. The poor woman was obsessed. She did not want to share *her* gorillas except with a very select few. There was no gorilla tourism there. What did the people who were giving up cultivatable land get out of it? The villagers in the Congo get some tangible benefits yet even so they must surely resent the rich tourists who pass through. Elephants are wonderful but if a troop of them go through your fields and devastate everything you might have second thoughts. If the local people don't share our views about their animals the poor animals don't have much of a future. I need a glass of wine, and then Molly needs a walk. Let's get Stanley from Paws."

Elena had boarded Stanley at Paws while she was in California consulting for RAND. She left instructions that we could walk him when we wanted to. I have no way of knowing whether Stanley welcomed our company which included Molly or whether he was quite content to be with his new friends at Paws. In any event, he trotted along with us and he and Molly exchanged some sniffs. They both marked the postbox. Stanley's presence raises a question I have tried to avoid thinking about. Molly is still a little too young to breed but the time is not far off. Stanley might make a suitable father but what about the puppies? There would be two or three and they certainly could not stay in the apartment. One dog was about all I was prepared to deal with. The people at Paws would take them on consignment, but if they did not sell, they would come back to me or go to the pound. Both of these choices seemed impossible to me. I will have to think about this. Meanwhile, Molly in her state of innocence trotted happily alongside Stanley.

When we got to the park I told Anne that if I had to be a biologist I would have liked to have been John Maynard Smith. "Who's that?" she asked. "Well he was born in 1920 in London where his father was a very successful surgeon who died when Maynard Smith was eight. He then moved to the country with his mother near where her parents lived. Her father was a very successful stockbroker and the family was well-off. Without any special encouragement Smith became interested in nature — identifying birds and the like. He was sent off to boarding school — ultimately Eton — which he hated. There was no science there and he was terrible in languages, so he was regarded as a somewhat stupid boy, save for his interest and abilities in mathematics. Just before he went 'up' to Cambridge, he had a family Sunday lunch and he told the assembled family that despite expectations he was not going to be a stockbroker. His grandfather demanded a statement of what he *was* going to be and Smiths said an engineer, an off-hand choice — so that is what he studied at Cambridge. He had been to Germany before the war to visit a relative and had actually heard a speech by Hitler. This persuaded him that there was going to be a war, and he joined the Communist Party in Cambridge because they seemed to be the only ones who took this seriously. Then there was war and Smith worked for several years as a designer of airplanes. He left the Communist Party after the Lysenko affair of the early 1950s. Trofim Lysenko was a crank scientist who persuaded Stalin that if you changed the characteristics of say wheat these acquired characteristics would be inherited so you could improve the crop this way. This went against everything that was known about genetics till then. Genes influence development, but development does not influence genes. But Lysenko got modern genetics outlawed in the Soviet Union, and anyone who persisted was sent to the Gulag. When Smith got into biology, he actually did an experiment on fruit flies. He conditioned some to have improved adaptation to heat. He bred them and their offspring had no special heat adaptation capabilities. Smith could see with his own eyes that Lysenko was wrong. But this came after he had decided to go back to college at age twenty seven. He knew he wanted to become an academic scientist but thought that theoretical physics was too hard so he chose biology. 'Any idiot can become a biologist', he later said.

"He enrolled at University College in London where the noted geneticist J.B.S. Haldane was the 'prof'. It turned out to have been a wonderful choice. Haldane also had been a Communist and had quit over Lysenko. He was also mathematically inclined. Smith did the experiments and the 'prof' would supply a mathematical model. But when Smith went to Sussex to create a new biology department, he had no time to do experiments, so he stopped being a 'wet' biologist and became what one might call a mathematical biologist. After he had set up the new department he was given a short leave and chose to go to the University of Chicago. He hated the city so he spent all his time working, and he came up with his most widely recognized idea, the notion of an 'evolutionary stable strategy' — ESS. You will see that it has a family resemblance to 'Nash equilibrium' which I told you about before. This is not an accident. Both of them are artifacts of game theory."

"Poor Nash," Anne said.

"He *did* win a Nobel Prize after all. Anyway Smith had for many years been exercised by a problem in animal behavior. Here are a few examples. Lions don't eat lions despite the fact that they eat almost everything else of the meat variety. As a rule animals do not fight to the death. The males make enough of a display so that an intruder decides it is better to back off. Butterflies like sun patches. The first male to arrive at one 'owns' it and other late-arriving male butterflies back off. The owner gets to mate with the females who come along. There is even a species that goes to the tops of hills. The first one up owns the territory. A naïve evolutionist might say they do this for the good of the species. But animals don't think about species so there must, Smith was sure, be another explanation and this must ultimately be expressed in the genes.

"This was an idea that already had its adherents including Haldane. Smith gave it the name 'kin selection'. The remark that I quoted before was something that Haldane was supposed to have said in a pub probably as a joke. To understand what he was getting at, much to my real regret, I have to introduce a few of those dreadful biological terms. Your genetic structure and mine is what is called 'diploid'. Your genes, and mine, are arranged in pairs one from your mother and one from your father."

"Prove it," says Anne.

"I will if you will give some blood to some biologist with a microscope."

"Not a chance," says Anne.

"Then you will have to take my word for it. Somewhere in one set there will be the genes that control the color of your eyes and in the other set there will also be genes that control the color but not necessarily the same color. That is why I have my mother's eye color but not my father's. If we should mate — I am talking hypothetically — then our offspring would get one set of the pair from me and one set from you. So if Haldane's goal is to preserve the family gene pool he will save two brothers. Nephews share a quarter of the genes so you will have to save four of them. Likewise you will have to save eight cousins. If you don't have eight cousins you are out of luck. I have often wondered how this would work in practice. You may have cousins you have never met. How would they identify themselves so that you can save them? Maybe you would say, 'Is anyone in danger of drowning here my cousin?' If you had an especially good gene you would lose it if you drowned, but the eight cousins might carry several copies among them and so the kin would benefit."

"Do you think that is how it really works?" Anne asked. "I'll tell you a story that Niels Bohr the physicist used to tell to cheer himself up. A young man in a shtetl in Russia was sent to Pinsk to hear the wonder rabbi. He came back and reported.

'The rabbi spoke three times. The first time was wonderful. The rabbi understood everything and I understood everything. The second time was even better. The Rabbi understood everything and I understood nothing.

But the third time was the best of all. The rabbi understood nothing and I understood nothing.'"

"What has that got to do with this?" Anne asked.

"Nothing," I answered.

"It was Smith who introduced game theory into evolutionary biology. This he did on his leave in Chicago when he got a book on the subject and read the first couple of chapters. He realized that there was a difference between the classical game theory of von Neumann, Morgenstern, and Nash and the application of game theory to genetics. In classical game theory you asked how would a rational opponent behave in view of the possibilities of certain moves. Roughly speaking, the Nash equilibrium occurs when both opponents agree that any further moves would not improve their situation. In evolutionary game theory, the question is what strategy improves the possibilities for breeding. The butterflies are an example. The first male occupant of a sun patch 'owns' it and any other male that comes along is an 'intruder' and leaves willingly. This is an evolutionarily stable strategy in Smith's sense, whereas the situation in which the occupant leaves when the intruder arrives is unstable. This simple idea opened the floodgates to game theory in biology. By the way in classical game theory, a game may have more than one Nash equilibrium, and in evolutionary game theory, there may be more than one evolutionarily stable strategy which might suggest a punctuated series of evolutionary steps.

"I would like to say something which I don't mean to be unkind. Smith was able to apply game theory to evolution after reading a chapter or so of a text. He was — he died in 2004 — a very clever man — really brilliant. But if he had decided to work on quantum mechanics or relativity, it would have required a lot more than one chapter in a text. You would need several courses. People could apply game theory to biology knowing only a fairly bare minimum of mathematics and it was 'Katy bar the door'. Look out! They soon discovered the 'prisoner's dilemma'. In the example I told you about, the logical choice was that we should both refuse to cooperate but the best choice was that we should both *choose* to cooperate. That was the dilemma. But real individuals do cooperate. How can we use game theory to explain this?

"Leave it to the biologists and game theorists. In my example we played one game. But suppose we used what we had learned in that game to play another and then another almost to *ad infinitum*. Here we may use strategies which exploit the knowledge of previous moves. A professor of political science at the University of Michigan, Robert Axelrod, had a wonderful idea. He invited all the game theorists he could get hold of to devise strategies for the prisoner's dilemma which could be programmed on a computer. Then the different strategies were turned loose to play against each other. A remarkable thing happened. The strategy that won was almost trivial. It is called Tit For Tat. You open with cooperate. If your opponent responds with cooperate so do you but if he, she, it, responds with defect, so do you. If your opponent continues to defect, so do you *ad infinitum* and you end up with the logical but subpar outcome. If your opponent catches wise and cooperates, you end up with the best outcome which is the cooperative one. All the other strategies that were tried did worse. Many biologists loved this. It pointed to a possible genetic explanation, they thought, of cooperative behavior. Richard Dawkins wrote a best-selling book about it, 'The Selfish Gene'. I think that Smith who was responsible for starting all of this had a more open mind. He thought that there might be some role to what he called 'group selection'. He invented something he called the 'haystack model'.

"He imagined some kind of animal that liked to live in groups in separate haystacks but from time to time they all meet together and mate before they return again to their separate haystacks. Suppose the animals in each haystack have one or two altruistic genes. But altruism costs. In Haldane's example you might drown to pass on your rare gene. The butterflies who give up without a fight lose an opportunity to breed. Within your group, the selfish individuals have a free ride. They benefit from whatever advantages the altruistic individuals produce without paying the cost. Hence, if all that was involved was individual selection, the altruistic gene would sooner or later disappear. But if you add up all the haystacks, the total number of altruistic genes is greater than the number of selfish genes — at least that is the idea. Hence, when the groups in the different haystacks meet, the altruistic genes are augmented. Smith produced a mathematical model for all of this but wasn't sure it had any application to the real world. It now seems as if there are species that show something of this kind of behavior at least statistically. I am always wary of statistics. There was the case of the disease that struck only men of fifty. Two cases had been reported — one of a boy of two and the other of a man of ninety eight. I think that Smith led a happy life. He apparently died while sitting upright in his chair.

"At the risk of annoying you I want to tell you one more thing about von Neumann since it is on the subject of genes."

"If you must," Anne said.

"I find this story interesting for a number of reasons. With Smith once he had published his work on game theory the flood gates opened. We can argue as to how important all of this was in the grand scheme of things. With von Neumann, it is just the opposite. In 1948 he gave a lecture which I will tell you about. In it he discussed how genetic reproduction had to work. This was years before the DNA revolution. No one at that lecture paid the slightest attention. I have the transcript with the questions that were asked and the program. There were people in the audience like Linus Pauling who won

two Nobel Prizes and who would devote years to the study of DNA who also
paid no attention. We have a copy of his program in which he flags a couple
of the lectures. Von Neumann's was not one of them. Max Delbrück, who
had been a physicist but later won a Nobel Prize for his work in genetics,
was also in the audience and he too asked no questions. Amazing.

# PROGRAM

### Monday, September 20

10:00 a.m. Welcome by Dr. L. A. DuBridge, President,
California Institute of Technology

The Hixon Fund and Introduction of Symposium Members
Dr. Max Mason, Chairman of the Hixon Committee,
California Institute of Technology

Plans for the Symposium. Dr. Lloyd A. Jeffress,
Hixon Visiting Professor of Psychobiology

2:00 p.m. Dr. H. W. Brosin, Chairman
Dr. John von Neumann, Speaker. *The Logic of Analogue
Nets and Automata*

4:00 p.m. Informal gathering in the lounge, Dabney Hall

### Tuesday, September 21

9:30 a.m. Dr. R. W. Gerard, Chairman
Dr. Lorente de Nó, Speaker. *Models of the Nervous System*

2:00 p.m. Dr. J. M. Nielsen, Chairman
Dr. Warren S. McCulloch, Speaker. *Why the Mind is in the
Head*

4:00 p.m. Informal gathering in the lounge, Dabney Hall

### Wednesday, September 22

9:30 a.m. Discussion meeting

### Thursday, September 23

Dr. H. S. Liddell, Chairman
Dr. K. S. Lashley, Speaker. *The Problem of Serial Order in
Behavior*

2:00 p.m. Dr. Paul Weiss, Chairman
Dr. Heinrich Klüver, Speaker. *Functional Differences between the Occipital and Temporal Lobes*

4:00 p.m. Members of the staff of the Biology Division will serve tea in
the Library, Kerckhoff Laboratories

"The symposium, which was called "The First Hixon Symposium on 'Critical Mechanisms and Behavior', took place beginning September 10, 1948. It was held at Caltech in Pasadena. Von Neumann spoke the first day. The title of his talk was 'The Logic of Adaptive Neural Systems', which could have meant anything and did not have much to do with his talk. The computer that von Neumann had worked on during the war, the ENIAC, had been turned on in the summer of 1947. By present-day standards, it was almost absurd. It stored data using vacuum tubes — nearly 18,000 of them. They ran hot and tended to blow out several a day which made the machine operable only about half the time. It used decimal arithmetic unlike its successors which ran on the yes–no of binary. It was programmed by women changing the wires as needed.

"Nonetheless, the thing could produce a ten-digit division quotient in a few thousandths of a second. It will not surprise you to learn that it was first used in the construction of the hydrogen bomb."

"Men! You seem to need wars to invent stuff like radar. It didn't take wars to invent the vacuum cleaner and it has done a lot more good for civilization than the hydrogen bomb. Sometimes you people make me sick."

"Don't look at me. I haven't invented anything. Getting back to von Neumann. He began his lecture with an apology saying that he was an outsider in most of the fields that were going to be discussed at the symposium. But he thought that it might be useful for him to describe the logic of computers to prepare the audience for the time when they might have to use them. Much of the first part of his lecture has to do with comparing the computer to the brain. This is what he spoke about at Harvard which blew me away and sooner or later out of mathematics. This part of his lecture is rather out of date. He was comparing the vacuum tube computer with the brain. I think his ideas of the complexity of the brain were right — it has so many neural connections that they could not all have been programmed but some must have been created at random. He also spoke a great deal about errors and how to correct them. This is the part that attracted all the attention in the question period. It is only towards the end of his lecture that he discusses the really important question — what is required for an automaton to reproduce copies of itself?

"As a rule, when we ask an automaton to produce something for us, the result is less complex than the automaton itself. For example, a 3D printer will produce a widget if we give it the appropriate instructions. What would it take for automata not only to reproduce themselves but also for the reproductions to be able to continue to reproduce themselves? Of course we might wonder if these reproductions could also mutate and so evolve as a species. Heady stuff, but let's stick to the self-reproduction.

"Von Neumann's discussion was pretty abstract which is probably why it went over everyone's head. A friend of mine recast it in more homey terms. Imagine that you have a machine shop which has all the tools you need to fabricate every tool in the machine shop. You also have a cabinet that contains the drawings for all these tools — the plans for making them — as well as a layout for the shop. This layout shows the details of this cabinet including its location. But what the cabinet does not contain are drawings of the drawings that are in the cabinet. This would lead to a never-ending process of drawings of drawings. It would begin to look like some crazy Marcel Duchamp construction on steroids. But the layout does contain the instruction 'copy all drawings and put them here in the cabinet'. This avoids the infinite regress.

"The machinist uses the drawings to make a new machine shop that contains everything but a new set of drawings. He uses the copy instruction to copy them and inserts them in the new machine shop's cabinet thus not only reproducing the original but also setting the seeds of the next replication. Von Neumann did this with abstract automata and showed how they could be arranged to self-replicate. He argued that any self-replication, including our own, had to have the same structure. This is what no one at the meeting got. We now know that the 'machinist' is the mechanism that links amino acids to make proteins. It is directed by reading 'drawings' — the genetic code carried by the messenger RNA which gets it from the DNA in our cells. Von Neumann foresaw all of this. He also discussed 'mutation', which involves alteration in the instructions and he mentioned the possibility that this might apply to genes. He wondered whether the 'natural gene' could ever contain enough information to contain a 'complete description' of the object to be reproduced. It is not clear what he meant by this object. As we know, DNA does contain a complete description which enables the double helix to be reproduced in the way von Neumann proposed.

"There it was, and no one paid the slightest attention. When five years later Crick and Watson discovered the double helix, they had never heard of this lecture, nor had anyone else in this community. It was only rediscovered years after the fact. I do not know whether von Neumann knew about these developments. In 1954, he was diagnosed with cancer which killed him three years later at age fifty four. He had created so much over his lifetime that he may have forgotten his brief remarks in a long-forgotten symposium. *Sic transit.*"

# Chapter 7

"I have no doubt that in reality the future will be vastly more surprising than anything I can imagine. Now my own suspicion is that the Universe is not only queerer than we suppose, but queerer than we *can* suppose."

J.B.S. Haldane

"Never, never, never, Faint heart never won fair lady!
Nothing venture, nothing win
Blood is thick, but water's thin
In for a penny, in for a pound
It's Love that makes the world go round!

Nothing venture, nothing win
Blood is thick, but water's thin
In for a penny, in for a pound
It's Love that makes the world go round!"

Gilbert and Sullivan

"The calla lilies are in bloom again..."

*Stage Door*

I am beginning to worry about the universe. I don't think it knows what it's doing. The expansion is accelerating and no one can explain why. I put an explanation in terms of "dark energy" on the same level as the elderly lady with her turtles. She explained to a lecturer on cosmology that the Earth rested on a giant turtle which rested on another turtle and so on. "What happens when the turtles run out?," the lecturer asked. "It's turtles all the way down," she explained. For all I know, dark energy is another turtle. Today, it was announced that the universe was older than it was thought to have been yesterday — some several billions of years older. What's the matter with these people? How can they miss several billions of years? Sometimes the universe appears to me like a game I once got for my birthday when I was a kid. There were no instructions. No one could figure out how to play it so we finally threw it away.

Molly and Anne have at least one thing in common — they don't care. Anne has told me categorically that she does not want to hear about the universe. She finds it impossible to relate to. Molly is Molly. So long as I feed her and take her to the park, that is all the universe she wants. Elena is back from California and comes to the park almost every day with Stanley. Anne tells me that Elena is "seeing someone" that she met in California; such an odd locution "seeing someone." I would take it as a given that Elena must have had a visual sighting of this person at some point. When you stop "seeing someone" does this mean that they can no longer enter your visual field? "You missed out on that one," Anne says, making Elena sound like some sort of subway. "The Lord works in mysterious ways," I answer. But the return of Elena and the presence of Stanley on an almost daily basis in the park has made my Molly problem acute. Should she have puppies? I have decided to have a talk with Doctor Levman. I am concerned that my lack of willingness to commit may have spilled over onto Molly.

I try to explain my problem to Doctor Levman over the phone. He says that I should come and see him and bring Molly. I make an appointment and go to the park near Doctor Levman's office first so that there will be no accidents that might be distracting. Molly seems a little dubious when we walk up the stairs to Doctor Levman's office. But he makes her feel at home and I give her a few treats. She lies down on the carpet and goes to sleep. "What are you thinking and feeling?," Doctor Levman asks me. I explain that I do not think I can deal with puppies. "That does not surprise me," Doctor Levman says. "What does surprise me is that you are able to share your life with someone else — albeit a dog. Why is that?" "I am also surprised," I answer. "Maybe it's because her demands are so clear. I never understand what women want and am always tripping over my good intentions." "Do you think that Molly wants puppies?," Doctor Levman asks. "How can I tell?" "But what do you think?" "I am glad I do not know because then I can decide if I want puppies. I see no good outcome. I can't deal with them and their futures would be in doubt. I can't stand the idea of bringing some helpless creatures into the world when I cannot predict their futures." "Then you have answered your own question," Doctor Levman said. "What about Anne? What does she think?" "She likes the *idea* of puppies but she has made it clear that she does not want to deal with an actual puppy." "What about you and Anne?," Doctor Levman asked, "She is my best friend," I answered. "How would you feel if she got involved with someone?" "Terrible," I answered. "Then don't you think you had better do something?," he asked. "She told me that she wouldn't touch me with a barge pole." "Faint heart never won fair lady," he answered. I thanked him, and Molly and I went home. My next step was to make an appointment with Doctor Snyder, who knew the original Molly.

"So this is Molly," Doctor Snyder says. "She looks the picture of health." Doctor Snyder has a wonderful way with dogs. They allow him to examine them even though it can be a little uncomfortable. He knows how to hold them. "What do you think is her problem?," Doctor Snyder asks. "It is really my problem," I answer, "I don't think that I can deal with puppies." Doctor Snyder looks surprised. "Didn't whoever sold her to you tell you? She can't have puppies. She is spayed. They try to do that when the dog is very young to avoid complications, but they should have told you." They probably did but the whole idea of having a dog was so overwhelming that I probably didn't listen. "If you have any papers which came with her I am sure that they will tell you." When I took Molly home I felt a little ashamed. I found her papers and sure enough there it is. That night I gave her an especially nice bone. She looked at me a little puzzled. I can't imagine what she was thinking. Now that that is over, I can go back to worrying about the universe.

I am quite sure that there are extraterrestrials even though we haven't seen any. I think I know what happened. A group of them landed in Dallas a few years ago in mid-summer wearing sombreros. They thought that would help them fit in. It was a hundred and five degrees in the shade, and the humidity was like Calcutta before the monsoon. They radioed the mother ship to come and pick them up at once and take them back to their own cool planet. The ship was disguised to look like a Greyhound bus, and it rolled into Dallas after having landed in a field somewhere nearby. The extraterrestrials got on board immediately and as soon as it got out of sight the bus took off. Some of them had to be revived on the bus with their planetary version of Gatorade, and all of them said that they would never come back to Earth again. If they had only landed in Paris in April, then I am sure the history would have been quite different. When I told this story to Anne, she asked, "Are you sure it was a Greyhound bus. It might have been a Trailways." "You may be right. It was moving pretty fast."

Anne is not happy with what happened to Molly. She wants to blame someone. I suppose we could blame the people at Paws but we do not know if they were responsible. They did not lie to us. If we had wanted a puppy who could have puppies we could have asked. It just never occurred to me. Probably the original owners of Molly approved of the operation. We will never know and I for one do not care. I love Molly as she is.

"Do *you* want puppies?," I asked Anne. "When I was young I thought all the time about having children." Anne answered, "I was going to name them after constellations. The first girl I was going to call *Ursa Minor*. She would explain that 'Minor' was her middle name and that it had been in the family for a long time. Then I got married and had to work to help get my husband through law school. After he went off I decided that I would have no living object in my apartment that I could not take to a bar. Not that I go to bars, but you know what I mean." "It must be very hard to be a woman," I remark. "It is but I practice nearly every day and besides there are perks." "Like what?" "Men give you their seats on the subway." "When was the last time that happened to you?" "About five years ago. It turned out that he was getting off and he nearly knocked me over. I think that you should marry doctor Levman." "I would except this would mean discussing his patients with him. Can you imagine anything more boring? Today a man came in to see me to discuss whether or not his dog should have puppies. For this I went to medical school?" "Let's take a trip together," I suggested. "I might," said Anne, "But only if we can sleep in separate cities." "How far apart do the cities have to be?"

I have had a chance to talk with Elena. She told me that she had been a math major at Harvard. "The people you knew are all gone." I asked her about a topologist that I had taken a course with. He seemed like a strange man. He got an idea for solving Boston's traffic problem. It was to make all the streets one way leading out of town. He was very serious and wrote many letters to the newspapers and showed up at meetings with the mayor. They finally had to lock him up in an institution. She had never heard of him. I told her about the one time that I made an impression on the chairman of the department. As a treat, someone from the astronomy department came over to show us a movie about solar flares. It was interesting for about the first two minutes. These eruptions kept popping up. But the chairman got the idea that the film was in upside down and had to be re-run right side up. I said that since the Sun was round what difference did it make? He never spoke to me again which I thought was a plus.

Elena told me that she had gotten her PhD in mathematical economics — game theory — at Harvard — and then had gone to work for RAND. "Anne told me that you tried to get a job at RAND," Elena said. "I was still a graduate student and I was not smart enough to be of any interest to them which I now look back on as a blessing. But Harman Kahn did try to persuade me that, all things considered, a nuclear war would not be so bad. I asked him if he had a shelter and the conversation ended." "The place has changed," Elena explained. "There are campuses all over the place although the headquarters are still in Santa Monica. You would probably recognize it. They still do military stuff although I do economic analysis. That is how I met my husband. But he got a job on Wall Street and we moved to New York. Then he got sick and that was the end of that. I think that Anne is angry at men. I am only angry at *him*. He had no right to do this to us. We were so happy. I would like to marry again but I am scared. By the way, Anne thinks that you really don't like women that much." "My father used to say about women, 'They are defective but they seem to be the best thing that has been invented along those lines so far'. I am not sure quite what he meant but it did seem important at the time. By the way, I hope Stanley will not feel frustrated when he realizes that Molly can't have his puppies although I am not sure how he will find out."

I have brought up the subject of the universe with Anne again. She refuses to discuss it unless I can tell her what happened before the Big Bang. "There was no 'before'," I explain. "That's nonsense," she says, "of course there was a before.

There is always a before." "Maybe we are one of several universes which developed from baby universes." "Show me," she says. I change the subject, "Which city would you like to visit that you haven't been to." "Venice," she answers at once. "Why?," I asked. "Do you remember the movie *Summertime* with Katharine Hepburn. She plays a middle-aged spinster school secretary named Jane Hudson from Akron, Ohio. She has saved up her money so she can take a trip to Venice. It is the fulfillment of a dream. The day after her arrival she sees a red glass goblet in an antique shop. It is an 18th century Murano glass but she does not know it. She just loves the color. The shop is owned by a man played by Rossano Brazzi — a gorgeous man. He comes on to her and in leaving the shop she tries to take a picture of it and falls into a canal. There is a certain amount of complication about whether or not the goblet is really an antique and what the status of Brazzi's marriage is. This is dealt with and they have an affair. She has never been so happy but decides that she has to go home. She has always stayed too long at parties. The last scene shows a train leaving with her and Brazzi running to catch up. He gives her a matching goblet. I cry every time I think about it. I saw the film at least five times. The scenes of Venice were wonderful. Did you see it?" "Yes, and I thought of a sequel. She returns to Akron and discovers that she is pregnant. A few years later she goes back to Venice with her son to introduce him to his father who does not have a clue." "You are card carrying moron," Anne says. "If you were not funny from time to time I would have nothing to do with you.

"I wanted to be Katharine Hepburn. I used to go around saying in what I thought was her voice, 'The calla lilies are in bloom again. Such a strange flower. Suitable to any occasion…'" Such an odd thing to say. Calla lilies are an African flower and are known locally as pig's ears. To change the subject, I told Anne that I had been trying to teach Molly to retrieve a ball. I had gotten a suitable ball from Paws but Molly showed no interest. I called Molly from the Kitchen and she came out. I gave her a treat. I then rolled the ball across the floor. Molly paid no attention. Anne took the ball and rolled it across the floor. Immediately Molly got the ball and returned it to Anne. "It's a girl thing," she explained. "Who did you want to be?" "Cary Grant," I said, "but in an interview he said that that was who *he* wanted to be so I gave up the idea since I felt that he had a head start. From a purely evolutionary point of view, what is the likelihood of creating Hepburn and Grant and having them star in *Bringing up Baby*?

"Now that I have brought up evolution I want to tell you something but von Neumann will come up again." "If you must, you must," Anne said.

"Darwin published *The Origin of Species* in 1859. Across the channel in Brno in what is now Czech Republic, Gregor Mendel, an Austrian monk, was in the middle of his plant breeding experiments. Mendel had a good scientific education and his role in the Augustinian Abbey Saint Thomas was to teach physics. He may have been inspired to begin his experiments by a teacher in the University of Olomouc who was studying the hereditary aspects of plants. There was an experimental garden in the monastery, and between 1856 and 1863, he cultivated some 29,000 pea plants. He could identify discrete properties of these plants. For example, some were short and some were tall. He discovered that if he bred short plants with short plants, the next generation would be all short and likewise tall with tall led to tall. But if he bred short with tall, in the next generation, ¾ of the plants were tall and ¼ were short. Mendel accounted for this by saying the hereditary results were determined by what he called 'factors', T for tall and t for short and that T was the dominant factor. So in breeding we produce TT, Tt, tT, and tt which accounts for the ratio. But one half of these tall plants also contain the short factor t. If these newly bred tall plants are allowed to self-pollinate they will reproduce the ¼, ¾ ratio. The same pattern occurred when he studied smooth and wrinkled seeds. We now see this as the gateway to the theory of evolution.

"Darwin never read Mendel's published papers and if he had he would have ignored them as having nothing to do with his theory of evolution. He saw traits evolving in small steps over millennia not in discrete jumps. But Mendel read Darwin. We have his annotated copy of the *Origin*. There is no reference whatever to the role of his experiments to the evolution to in the evolution. What he is worried about is whether Darwin's theory is compatible with his Catholic faith. It took work in the beginning of the 20th century to rediscover Mendel's laws. The 'factors' became 'genes' and the connection with evolution was acknowledged. Nonetheless, there was no understanding of the mechanism.

"Von Neumann did not reveal the biology. What he did do was to make clear what the biology must do. He understood the role of the transfer of information. Remember my little story about the machine shop and the cabinet that contained the drawings — the plans — for reproducing everything in the machine shop except the drawings of the drawings themselves. What has to happen when you make a new machine shop you must copy the drawings and insert the copies into the new shop. Put abstractly, you must extract the information in the drawings and transfer it to make a new set of drawings. The key thing here is the transfer of information. But this is what a computer does. It transfers the information contained in a program to the machine so it can do something. Von Neumann understood that in self-replication there must be a way of extracting and transferring the information contained in the gene. A kind of RNA transmits the code in the DNA to another form of RNA called messenger RNA. There are the ribosomes that read the messenger RNA like tape recorders and construct the amino acid chains out of which the proteins are built. I have short-circuited the details which give me something of a headache but that is the idea. It is the way that von Neumann said it should be and none of the people who discovered it had ever heard of his lecture."

"You know what your problem is?," Anne asks. "You read too much. I think that you should take tango lessons. You will feel much better."

*Chapter* **8**

www.ourworldtravels.com

"If you are afraid of loneliness, don't marry"

Chekov

Anne has agreed to take a trip to Venice with me. I will explain the deal in a minute, but my idea is to let her realize as much as possible her fantasy about Katharine Hepburn and "Summertime." Anne is about the same age that Hepburn was at the time she made the film. Hepburn was born in 1907 and the film was made in 1954. They look a bit alike. Like Anne, Hepburn was briefly married when she was very young. However, I don't see Hepburn helping anyone through law school. Maybe Anne would jump into a Venetian canal. Not without a hazmat suit I hope. That jump made Hepburn quite sick. There is a moment in the film that has a special appeal for women. She has come out of Brazzi's shop and is walking away with a spirited sense of dignity when she trips, spoiling the impression she is trying to make. This was a pure Hepburn invention and it surprised the director David Lean who thought she really had tripped. Hepburn had the idea that she and her small entourage would live on Murano out of the Venetian hurly burly in a house near the studio from which Lean worked. The place had a tennis court and a pool but turned out to be a dump from which they fled. Lean was living in Venice at the Gritti Palace — a 4-star hotel on the Grand Canal. Hepburn and her people rented a two-story apartment with three bedrooms, a cook, butler, and maid, and their own gondolier across from it. I cannot duplicate the apartment, but I can install Anne in the Gritti. Following our understanding of not sleeping in the same city, I have installed myself on the Lido. Molly is boarded at Paws. I wish I could have explained to her that it was only going to be for just about a week. Elena will take her for walks in the park with Stanley.

The Lido is sort of an afterthought to Venice. It is basically a sandbar surrounded by water — the lagoon on one side and the Adriatic Sea on the other. You get from Venice to the Lido in *vaporetti* — water busses that used to run on steam. They now run on a twenty-four-hour schedule and have various stops in Venice. I had not visited the Lido on my earlier trips to Venice since I did not especially want to go to the beach and there was so much to see in the city. But then I took a bicycle trip from Venice to Florence and our departure hotel was on the Lido. We could bicycle to the end of the island and then take a ferry to the mainland to continue our trip. I arrived a few days early and came to very much like the Lido. It is not much of a tourist attraction apart from the beach. The hotels are more modest and family-run. The exception is the Grand Hotel des Bains in which movie stars used to stay and where Thomas Mann wrote his homoerotic novel

*Death in Venice*, which was published in 1912. The nice thing is that many people who actually work in Venice live on the Lido so you can commute with them in the morning and in the evening when they return, unless you have a late night in Venice.

I suggested a *modus operandi* to Anne. I would pick her up at about ten and we could then spend the day sightseeing and then I would go home to the Lido after dinner. The nightlife in Venice is really not worth staying up for. Therefore, in the mornings I took an early vaporetto along with the people who were working in Venice. Then I would get off at the stop at San Marco and follow some of them to some nearby café to have an Americano and listen to the gossip — whatever of it I could understand. I love the Italian language. A musical direction like "*adagio ma non trope,*" expresses a whole way of life. Or what about "*se non è vero, è ben trovato*"? If you can say it well enough, it does not matter if it is true. That is a perfect definition of fiction. I find Italians much kinder about sharing their language than the French who have limited patience with tourists altogether. On my Venice bike trip, I got lost outside a town where we were staying the night. I had forgotten the name of the hotel except that I knew it was somewhere near the center of town — *il centro*. As I was riding my bike, wondering what to do next, I noticed a distinguished looking middle-aged man mowing his lawn. I asked politely "*dove e' il thentro prego*" falling unwittingly into the Spanish pronunciation of the "c". He stopped his mowing and came over to study me. Then he said "*dove e' il chentro*" and made me say it a few times before he gave me the directions. Once, in France, I went to buy a knife with a number of blades and other things. I mistakenly asked whether the proprietress had Swiss army knives. She said no but she had a French army knife and, if it made me happy, she would paint a white cross on it. It was a time when the French franc was collapsing. I asked her if she took French money.

After my café stop I walked over to the Gritti. I let Anne decide what she wanted to see. In Venice, I am happy simply walking more or less aimlessly to see what shakes out. On my previous visits, around lunchtime I would follow what looked to me like a knowing Venetian couple to see where *they* had lunch. This way, I had compiled a nice little list of local favorites which I could share with Anne. Venice is a great place for gelati which was one of our afternoon stops. After three days of this, I said that she might like a day of rest and a swim. Apart from a few passing jellyfish, the Adriatic off the Lido is quite safe to swim in. Also, she would have a chance to see how the other half lived. I told her how to find the *vaporetto* which went to the Lido, and I told that I would meet her at the pier. The next morning, she showed up with a little bag containing her swimming gear including a very luxuriant towel from the hotel.

Our route to the beach took us by the Grand Hotel des Bains.

*Grand Hotel des Bains*
venice, italy

We have both re-read *Death in Venice*. On previous visits I have tried to find without success traces of Mann in the hotel. I suggest we give it another try. The place is undergoing renovations, but I tell the foreman that Anne and I shared a *letto matrimoniale* in the hotel a few years ago and that we have come back for sentimental reasons. "What is that," Anne asked, "A double bed," I explain to which she responds, "Hmmm." We get to walk around and find no traces of Mann. This does not surprise me. About the time that Mann was staying on the Lido, Proust was staying in the Grand Hotel in Cabourg in Normandy which became Balbec in his novel. On another bike trip, I spent a couple of nights in the Grand Hotel in Cabourg. Proust was everywhere. There were photos, a bust, and dedicated rooms — all in full view. The Hotel is on the Promenade Marcel Proust.

Proust is regarded as a French national treasure. Mann, on the contrary, was a German in Italy and the subject of his novella is not likely to encourage tourists. It is not called *Death in Venice* and not *A Death in Venice* for no reason. There are two protagonists in the novella, the writer Gustav von Aschenbach and cholera. The disease hovers over the novella like a shroud. In fact in 1911, when Mann visited the Lido, there was a cholera epidemic in Venice. There were 778 cases with 262 deaths. It is not difficult to understand why there is no bust of Mann at the Grand Hotel des Bains.

The real Mann was going through something of a writer's slump. The two-volume semi-autobiographical novel *Buddenbrooks*, written in his twenties, had created a sensation, but now in his mid-thirties, he had written nothing comparable since. Aschenbach was in his fifties and was also in a writing slump. Aschenbach was a widower while Mann had come to the Lido with his wife at the same time of year — June. Both stayed in the same hotel. Both took walks in the direction of the Hotel Excelsior — the sister hotel. In the lounge that first day, Aschenbach saw the beautiful Polish boy Tadzio of about fourteen along with his sisters. In the dining room that first day, the real Mann saw the real Tadzio, who later became Baron Wladyslaw Moes, along with his sisters. Mann was absolutely fascinated by the boy but did not pursue him. The boy was ten and was completely unaware of Mann's interest until the film *Death in Venice* came out in 1971.

Aschenbach became obsessed with Tadzio, but the weather began to wear on him. There was a *sirocco*, a heated wind, that blew on the city and made the lagoon "ill-smelling." He decided that he had to leave and indeed got as far as the train station to find that his trunk had been shipped to the wrong destination so he had to return to the hotel. On his subsequent visits to Venice from the hotel, he felt that something was wrong. The place had an odd smell like the interior of a hospital. But he was assured that it was nothing — just a temporary effect of the *sirocco*. It was only when a British travel agent in Venice told him the truth — there was a plague of cholera — that he realized that had to leave Venice immediately. He could not find the courage to warn Tadzio's mother to leave with her children, and he had himself "made up" by the barber to look more youthful. As the novella ends, Aschenbach was described as being on the beach observing Tadzio roughhousing with some other boys. He seemed to gesture at Aschenbach. But he had just died of cholera.

"You wonder why there is no bust of Mann in the hotel?," Anne asks. "Do people still read Mann?," I wondered. "In my day at Harvard there were the big three — Proust, Joyce and Mann. If you could not discuss *The Magic Mountain*, no Radcliffe girl would even have coffee with you. If you had read both volumes of *Buddenbrooks* in translation, you might be invited to be someone's date at a Jolly Up, and if you had read them in the original, there is no telling what you might have gotten. It was a form of natural selection." "I thought that acquired characteristics were not inherited," Anne notes. "They aren't but most Radcliffe girls didn't know this." By now we had reached the cabana which my hotel had supplied on its portion of the beach. We retreated to our separate locker rooms to change.

When Anne returns, she is wearing a stunning bikini. "I bought it yesterday," she explains. My thought is that it would get a Dominican friar to regret his vows. "What do you think of the color?," she asks. "The man in the store assured me that it is the same blue that Manet used in his paintings of Venice." "*Se non è vero*," I thought, but only said that it was a beautiful color.

We swam and then went for lunch at a taverna near the beach. After we had sat down, Anne said, "I have a confession." My heart sank. I thought that life had repeated art, while Hepburn had fallen in love with the seller of red Murano glass goblets, Anne had fallen in love with the seller of blue bikinis. "It is the hotel," she went on. "It is a wonderful hotel and they couldn't be nicer to me and I appreciate being across the street from where Hepburn stayed, but it is just too much. I only brought one pair of glass slippers. If you could find me a simpler hotel here on the Lido, that would make me very happy." After lunch, we looked around and found a very nice hotel with a garden. I checked her in and we went back to Venice to collect her things. I told her to keep the beach towel as a souvenir. I told the people at the Gritti that a family emergency had arisen. They were understanding. That night at dinner, Anne said, "You know that you are a very nice man, but don't let it go to your head."

# Chapter 9

"Everything goes past like a river and the changing tastes and the various shapes of men make the whole game uncertain and delusive. Where do I find fixed points in nature, which cannot be moved by man, and where can I indicate markers by the shore to which I ought to adhere?"

Immanuel Kant

Leonhard Euler: $e^{i\pi} = -1$

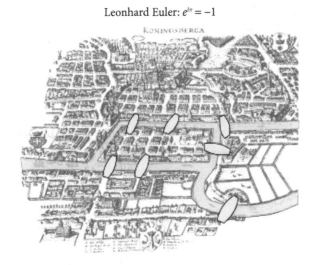

## I

There are two very nice seasons in New York — spring and fall. The winters can be very tough. The winds come off the East River and the Hudson and produce a damp cold, which is hard to dress for. Sometimes, we have ice which makes the sidewalks a sort of malignant ice rink. And the summers are infernal. I gather that in Calcutta a mitigating plea for a crime of violence is that it was committed in the pre-monsoon season. If you have even been there at that time you will understand why. I think something similar might be reasonable for New York in the summer. Of the two good seasons, I like the fall the best. I like the light and often the days are clear and sunny. Sometimes in the spring you get days of temperatures in the nineties which remind you of what is coming. Where I live, in Greenwich Village, and there is a nearby Italian restaurant — Silvio's — where I go a lot in the fall. They have a big terrace which is wonderful for people-watching. Silvio claims that all sorts of movie stars eat at his restaurant, but I have never seen one or at least one that I recognized. I usually come around five and install myself on the terrace until it is time to order. Silvio calls me "professore" because I read books on the terrace. I call him "dottore" because it amuses him. Silvio never asks me what I am reading or why. I am now reading Immanuel Kant's *Critique of Pure Reason* and I am not entirely sure why. I guess his life story intrigues me. He was born in Königsberg in what was then Prussia in 1724 and, until he died in 1804, he never moved farther than sixty miles from Königsberg. I don't know why. Maybe he was trying to solve the problem of the seven bridges. I will tell you about that later but first I want to describe the woman who sat down at a table not far from mine.

I had sat down at my favorite table with a clear view of 6<sup>th</sup> Avenue. I have ordered a glass of Brunello di Montalcino. Silvio only serves this by the glass to customers he likes. It comes from near his home in Tuscany and is a treasure. One of his waiters comes with a bruschetta,

"A present from the chef," he tells me. I open my book. I have not gotten beyond the first two paragraphs of the introduction. The first reads, "That all our knowledge begins with experience there can be no doubt. For how is it possible that the faculty of cognition should be awakened into exercise otherwise than by means of objects which affect our senses, and partly of themselves produce representations, partly rouse our powers of understanding into activity, to compare to connect, or so separate these, and so convert the raw materials of our sensuous impressions into a knowledge of objects, which is called experience? In respect of time therefore, no knowledge of ours is antecedent to experience, but begins with it." I take a sip of my wine and begin to turn this paragraph over in my mind when a taxi draws up in front of the restaurant and a woman gets out.

In the next paragraph, Kant distinguishes between *a priori* knowledge, which precedes and is indeed independent of experience, and *a posteriori* knowledge, which is derived from experience. Any experience of knowledge is a blend of the two. I am digesting this when the descending woman exhibits a very attractive pair of legs. I knew *a priori* that this woman had two legs but that they were this attractive I could only know *a posteriori*. The rest of the woman emerges from the taxi. She is wearing a black dress with some sort of reddish scarf that sets if off. I am not good at describing people's faces. I would make a very poor eyewitness. Put simply, she is a very beautiful woman — perhaps not the kind that could stop traffic but the kind that could break your heart. She asks for a table for two and orders a San Pellegrino. Her table is close enough to mine that I can see what she ordered. Usually this does not merit a bruschetta, but the waiter delivers her a gift from the chef. This means that Silvio has seen her and shares my opinion. She opens a copy of the *New Yorker* and begins to read. We will come back to her later, but first, I want to tell you about my dream.

## II

Last night I had a dream about Kant. He had come to New York to lecture at NYU and wanted my advice. I did not recognize him at first because he was not wearing the wig that the portraits of him always show. But he introduced himself speaking in slightly accented English. In particular, he wanted to know what "Neo-Kantians" were. I told him that they were people who had decided after some reconsideration that he was right. "I knew I was right," he said. He had come to my apartment in Greenwich Village. "What do you think about my clothes?," he asked. "The suit is ok, but we will have to do something about the shoes." "I had them made in Königsberg. They were very fashionable at the time. All my clothes were fashionable once I got some money." There was a Payless shoe store on 6ᵗʰ Avenue not far from my apartment and Kant agreed to walk there with me.

It was only when we stood side by side I realized how short he was. He barely came up to my shoulder. When we got to 8ᵗʰ street, he explained, "I was so small at birth that no one thought I was going to live. We had no money for doctors but somehow I pulled through. I was very weak as a child and young man but I got an idea. If I went on very fast walks I would take in a lot of air and this would cure me. So I got into the habit of daily walks.

Do you know Königsberg?" I had to admit that I didn't. "Well it is built on the two sides of the Pregel River. Between the sides there are two islands in the river Lomse and Kneiphof. The Albertina University is on Kneiphof Island. I started there when I was sixteen and spent most of my life there. The Königsberg Cathedral is also on this island. Once I had the choice I never went there but I am buried there. From time to time I visit my tomb. It is very relaxing."

Kant finished picking out a nice pair of loafers at Payless, although he insisted on keeping his Königsberg shoes. It was getting close to dinnertime, so I suggested that we might have a coffee at Starbucks. I planned to have dinner at Silvio's. I thought that Silvio would enjoy meeting a real professor. Kant ordered a decaf skinny latte and I had my usual espresso. "I would like to tell you more about my walks," he said. "In my days there were seven bridges that enabled you to get across the branches of the river. The last one built connected the two islands. It was called the Hönigbrücke — the Honey Bridge — because it took a bribe of a large barrel of honey to get permission to construct it. Four of the other bridges went from Kneiphof Island to one of the banks and two went from Lomse. Here is a sketch. It looks pretty complicated but you can see the bridges.

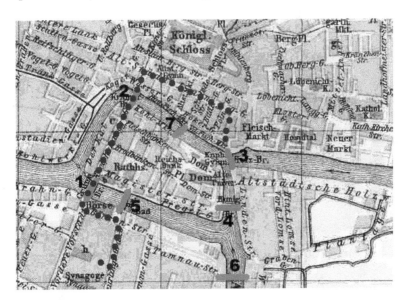

"What I always did on my walks was to cross all seven bridges. It did not matter in which order I crossed them or even where I started but I had to cross all seven. To make the walks more interesting I tried to find a path so that I never had to cross the same bridge twice. I did this for forty years and never could find one. I always had the feeling that there was something *a priori* involved but I never could get hold of it and neither could anyone else in Königsberg."

We sat on the terrace at Silvio's and he came out to join us. I introduced them. "This is Professor Kant. He has come to give a lecture at NYU." "I am honored professore. I will drink a glass of wine with you." A whole bottle of Brunello di Montalcino was produced, and Kant pronounced it excellent. "May I suggest a menu?," Silvio asked. Kant agreed. "Start with the *Antipasto Toscana* — this is from the region of Italy where I was born. Then have the *Bistecca alla Fiorentina per Due* and then an *Insalata Mista di Stagioni*. I would suggest that you try the *Vino nobile di Montepulciano*, an excellent wine." Kant again agreed. He ate with great relish. As we were walking back to my apartment, he said, "That was an excellent meal. Much better than what I usually get now."

## III

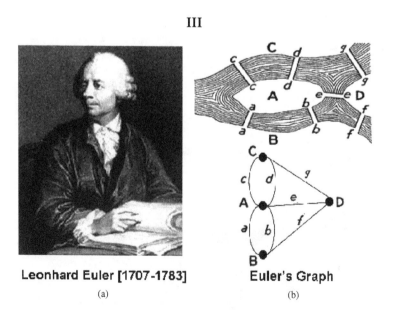

**Leonhard Euler [1707-1783]**          **Euler's Graph**

(a)                                                    (b)

Mathematics and music have in common the fact that genius is discovered early. Leopold Mozart began giving keyboard lessons to his daughter 'Nannerl' when she was seven. Her toddler brother Wolfgang climbed up to the keyboard and began reproducing the chords. It was not long afterward when Wolfgang and Nannerl began performing at courts, and it was not long after that that Leopold realized with some considerable regret that as a composer his son was going to totally overshadow him. Leonhard Euler's Swiss pastor father Paul realized that his son had special abilities. At the age of thirteen. he entered the University of Basel where he studied theology, Greek, and Hebrew. His father wanted him to become a pastor. People with great mathematical gifts simply cannot conceal them. To his great credit, Paul Euler decided to give his son an opportunity. He was friendly with the Bernoulli family and the senior member, Johann, was considered to be one of the best mathematicians in Europe. He tutored young Euler on Saturday afternoons and quickly realized that Euler was a mathematical genius in the making. Bernoullii had two sons — Daniel and Nicolas — who were teaching at the Imperial Russian Academy of Sciences in St. Petersburg. Nicolas, who was teaching physiology, died and his brother recommended Euler for the job. Euler arrived there in 1727 and soon moved over to the mathematics department where he stayed until 1741 when he took a position at the Berlin Academy where he spent the next twenty five years. Euler's contributions to mathematics would take volumes to describe, but what concerns us here is a little work he did in 1736 in which he solved the problem of the seven bridges of Königsberg. I do not know how he had heard of this problem. Maybe he passed through the town on his way to St. Petersburg, although in his paper he says that the problem was "widely known." This is a problem where the method of solution turned out to be much more important than the problem itself. It started a new branch of mathematics — the theory of graphs.

Mathematicians deal in abstractions. What is remarkable is that these abstractions sometimes apply to the real world. Euler turned the problem of the seven bridges of Königsberg into an abstraction — a graph. The civic structures on the two islands and the river banks are an irrelevance. So is the nature of the seven bridges. The whole thing can be replaced by an abstract graph. The little circles A and D represent the two islands and B and C the two banks. The seven bridges are the lines a, b, c, d, e, f and g. Things have been moved around in a way that does not change the problem. This is the topological nature of it. This use of topological ideas was one of the major innovations in Euler's solution. Viewed this way, the solution becomes possible without trying to enumerate all the walks. During the walk, one enters a bridge and leaves by a bridge. There are, for example, five bridges emanating from A. Any transit of A uses two bridges — one arriving, one leaving. Two transits uses four bridges (since the same bridge can't be used twice). The only way to use all five bridges touching A exactly once each is to start or end at A and transit it twice. For B a similar argument leads to the conclusion that B must be a beginning or end point and be transited once. The same applies to C and D, each of which, like B, is the end point of three bridges. Conclusion: *Every* "land mass" — A, B, C, and D — must be an end point. Since there can be only two end points, a walk of the seven bridges crossing each bridge only once is not possible. Euler's reasoning was a little different, but he also took account of the fact that an odd number of bridges touch each land mass. And he generalized the problem to any number of land masses and any number of bridges (he was, after all, a mathematician).

So the problem of the seven bridges of Königsberg can be solved without actually taking a single walk. When did the people of Königsberg understand that all their walking in search of such a path had been a waste of time?

Kant had a favorite teacher at the university named Martin Knutsen. Knutsen had tried to understand Newtonian physics. When a comet appeared in 1698, Knutsen predicted that it would re-appear in the winter of 1744. Indeed, a comet did reappear as predicted. His published prediction came to Euler's attention and Euler decided that Knutsen's mathematics were nonsense. In fact, the 1744 comet was a different object. Knutsen was not persuaded and his popularity as a teacher was undiminished. But when Kant published his first work on cosmogony, he sent a copy to Euler with a note that read in part, "The world sees in you esteemed sir, the individual who better than others is in a position to rescue the human understanding from its protracted error and perplexity concerning the most intricate points of Mechanics, and it is just this that moves me to solicit most respectfully your precise and gracious approval of these poor thoughts…. If you do me the honor of either publishing or sending me privately your treasured judgment of this modest work, I shall then begin to have a certain respect for it."

Euler does not seem to have replied to this letter nor does he seem to have told Kant that he had solved the problem of the seven bridges of Königsberg.

## IV

Kant was a popular teacher and led an active social life, which included playing a good deal of billiards. He had also developed a decent reputation as a philosopher when for no reason anyone could discern he dropped out. He was forty six. His isolation lasted ten years. When one of his former students wrote him, he answered, "My great thanks, to my well-wishers and friends, who think so kindly of me as to undertake my welfare, but at the same time a most humble request to protect me from any disturbance." When he finally emerged in 1781, he had written the 800-page manuscript of the *Critique of Pure Reason*. At first, it did not receive much attention, but after a few years, it was recognized as a philosophical masterpiece and Kant was invited to lecture everywhere but chose never to leave Königsberg. One thing you will not find in the *Critique* or indeed in any of Kant's works is a discussion of women. Even Socrates had a wife — Xanthippe. It is sometimes said that he married her because she could give him a good argument. Kant had none. I doubt that he ever had a girlfriend. Maybe when he was young, girls made fun of him because of his small body and large head. There were no girls in his school. Women were barely educated in Königsberg. He would have been of no use in trying to understand the young woman who was sitting a few tables from me at Silvio's. I noticed that she made a few attempts to call someone on her cellphone. There was no answer. She ordered an appetizer.

When I left my table and passed hers, I noticed two things. The appetizer had been served with a half bottle of Brunello di Montalcino and she had been crying. I also realized that I had seen this woman before under very different circumstances. It was in a bookstore, and she had helped me to find a book. It was Anne. Later, when I knew her better, she told me that she had recognized me from the store but did not want to say anything. She was too upset. She had had a date with her estranged husband whom she still loved and hoped to reconcile with. He had never appeared and had never even sent a message of regret. It was then that she filed for divorce.

### V

I had another dream about Kant. He was wearing a natty blue blazer and a Kangol hat. He was also wearing the loafers he had bought at Payless. I congratulated him about his attire. "You know," he said, "that when I was a student I was so poor that I had to borrow clothes when mine were being mended." He wanted to discuss women. "You know that the only two women I was really acquainted with were my mother and my sister. My mother died when I was thirteen and my sister took care of me when I was old and not in my right mind. Tell me about women." "That," I said, "would take many more dreams."

# Chapter 10

"To the reign of **Queen Anne**, naught compares
When it comes to fine tables and chairs,
But in matters dynastic
'Twas less than fantastic:
She'd plenty of grace but no heirs."

"May the parents of your children become rich."

Austrian wedding toast

"Salud, dinero y amor...."

Spanish wedding toast

"It's the accessories that complete the look"

A woman in the gym

"In most species, the female does most or all of the nest construction, though the male often helps."

Wikipedia

## I

It was a simple wedding. Neither of us had any family. Elena was the bridesmaid and Doctor Levman was my best man. He had always told me that he would not express an opinion about whether or not I should get married. He just wanted to give me the choice since I seemed not to be able to give myself one. I think he was pleased at what I had chosen to do. He liked Anne who had come with me to talk to him. Mrs. Levman was there. She looked like the sort of woman on whose generous lap one would place one's head and cry one's heart out. I would imagine that after a day of listening to people's impossible emotional problems, that's what he did. Or maybe they went to the movies. Or maybe they went to parties with other psychoanalysts and told jokes like that of the two behavior analysts who meet in an elevator and one says to the other, "You're fine. How am I?"

Of course, Molly and Stanley were there. I have no idea what they were thinking. They pretty much kept to themselves. I knew a judge who lived in my building. He had been a math major at Princeton and like me had decided that doing original mathematics was not for him. We did talk some mathematics. He was very happy to perform the ceremony. Anne initially wanted to talk to me about what she should wear. Should she wear white? I told her that she would look beautiful in whatever she wore. "That is a Mickey Mouse answer," she said, "I want a real opinion." "In that case," I said, "I would like blue." "I am glad you said that," she answered, "blue is one of my best colors and I can wear the pin that I bought in Venice." Silvio was there. It was at his restaurant where I first really saw Anne. He was going to make a feast for us at his restaurant.

I owe an explanation for how all of this came about.

After we came home from Venice, we found that we missed each other's company. Of course, we could still see each other as before, but there was something unsatisfying about this. Neither of us spoke to the other about it since I guess we both were afraid of rejection. Anne's failed marriage left her profoundly wounded, and she had made so many cynical remarks about my inability to have a real relationship with a woman that I did not want to say anything either. I thought that I might suggest another trip. Anne had studied French in college and kept up with it by going to all the events at the French Institute at NYU. She sometimes asked me to speak French with her. I was almost bilingual as a result of living in France and studying the language intensively. I had also had had a French girlfriend. She once asked me to Sunday lunch with her parents. They asked her what my intentions toward her were. "None," she said. We had lunch in a restaurant. But Anne had never been to France. When she was trying to put her husband through law school, there had not been enough money, and when he left her, it knocked the wind out of her. She had always wanted to go to Paris, and now I could give her the chance.

**II**

Au troisième temps de la valse
Nous valsons enfin tous les trois
Au troisième temps de la valse
Il y a toi, y a l´amour et y a moi
Et Paris qui bat la mesure
Paris qui mesure notre émoi
Et Paris qui bat la mesure
Laisse enfin éclater sa joie.

Jacques Brel, Valse a Mille Temps

Of course, on Anne's first visit, we would see the classic sights — like the Louvre and Notre Dame. I thought we should stay in a Left Bank hotel, a bit out of the usual tourist traffic. I chose the Madison on the Boulevard St. Germain. It was an upbeat hotel without the deluxe of the Gritti Palace. There were hotels in the Latin Quarter that were a bit suspect. A friend of mine stayed in one and left his shoes outside his door with the expectation that they would be polished by the morning. In fact, they vanished. When he complained to the owner, the response was "*Mais monsieur c'nest pas un hotel deluxe.*" I planned to take Anne on a night cruise on a *bateau- mouche*. In my days, they were anchored cabarets. I first heard, Barbara — the stage name of Monique Andrée Serf — sing her song *Göttingen* there. She was very tall and dressed entirely in black. She had spent the war hiding from the Germans but had written this beautiful song of reconciliation. Now the boats cruised the Seine by night and offered dinner. For a supplement, you could top the night off by a visit to a nightclub like the Crazy Horse, which we skipped. But I had my own agenda, which I explained to Anne.

In my math days, I had had a tutor who took a year off in Paris. He told me about Bourbaki. There was a 19th century French general named Charles Denis Bourbaki, whose career seems to have been somewhat mixed. For reasons quite unclear, in the mid-1930s a group of French mathematicians decided to call themselves Nicolas Bourbaki. Henceforth, they would publish under this pseudonym. They had decided that the mathematics they found lacked rigor and they were going to correct this. They began producing a series of books which they called *E'le'ments de mathe'matique*. Originally, they were all from the *École normale supérieure*, one of the *grandes e'coles* located in this instance in the Latin Quarter. But then they opened their membership to some mathematicians from the College de France. They began to have communal lunches at a nearby restaurant called Aux Trois Bourriques. *Burricus is* Latin for a small horse — a burro. Why the restaurant has this name I have no idea. You won't find it in the standard restaurant guides, although the food is excellent. That is probably why the mathematicians chose it. My tutor told me about the lunches. When I first went there I asked the owner where the mathematicians ate and booked a table nearby so I could overhear them. I admit that this was a bit of voyeurism, but I could not resist. And now I could show it to Anne. I also took her to the Théâtre de la Huchette.

This tiny theater which is on the street with the same name began in 1957 and is still running. It is devoted to the plays of one writer, Eugene Ionesco. When it began, Ionseco's plays like *La Cantatrice Chauve* had an appeal to a limited audience — just enough to fill the theater. Now they are considered classics and still fill the theater. He had a connection with another odd French group that called themselves Oulipo. These were writers who were seeking new forms. Georges Perec, who wrote the great French novel *La Vie Mode d'Emploi*, was a member. This was not really an Oulipian novel, but to make up for it, he wrote a three hundred-page novel which did not use the letter "e" and which is a mystery in which the absence of the letter "e" plays an essential part. Ionesco was less interested in these literary tricks. Anne found the performances wonderful. I also wanted Anne to experience some of the great Parisian restaurants such as La Tour 'd Argent. It had lost a few stars, but it is in a magnificent site within eyeshot of Notre Dame. If you order the pressed duck you will later get a post card with the duck's number. The wine cellar is so valuable that it has an armed guard — altogether not to be missed.

We chose to go there on one of those warm misty nights that Paris has in the spring. It was a short walk from the hotel. Anne was wearing high heels. On the way back, she tripped on a bit of rough sidewalk, and I caught her. She was in my arms and we held each other tightly. A great wall had come tumbling down and our emotions tumbled over the top like a cascading waterfall. Nothing was said. Nothing had to be said. Back at the hotel she led me to her room.

The next morning I suggested that we trade in our two rooms for one junior suite. She agreed but then said, "Look, I know you kiddo. You have had no practice with living with women. Molly does not count. She does not get a vote and I do. You are promising but need serious work. Once the suitcases are moved, I am sending you to the Café Flore while I make a nest. I will come and get you when I am done. You will only get in my way while I am working." I sat in the Flore with my croissant and coffee until Anne came and got me. Thus, began our life together.

CPSIA information can be obtained
at www.ICGtesting.com
Printed in the USA
BVHW060337220920
589329BV00002B/7

9 789811 218194